FLOWER AND PLANT PRODUCTION

in the Greenhouse

KENNARD S. NELSON, B.A., M.S., Ph.D.

Formerly Extension Specialist in Floriculture,
The Ohio State University

FLOWER AND PLANT
PRODUCTION

in the Greenhouse

THE INTERSTATE PRINTERS & PUBLISHERS, INC.
Danville, Illinois

To . . .

Prof. Alex Laurie

PREFACE

The production of flowers and plants in the greenhouse is a fascinating occupation, and it is one that is becoming increasingly more technical as new information on the growth and development of plants becomes available. There have been many advancements in the knowledge and understanding of the growth of plants in the greenhouse. There is a constant need for better informed workers for greenhouses—growers who not only have a genuine interest in the production of greenhouse crops but who have a sound concept of plant growth and the effect of the surroundings on this growth.

This is an introductory text for individuals who are not acquainted with the floriculture industry. It is hoped that the readers will gain a general view of the way in which this industry operates; some specific knowledge of plant growth in the greenhouse and ways to promote it; and possibly most important, some suggestions on how more training and information can be obtained.

KENNARD S. NELSON

Columbus, Ohio

TABLE OF CONTENTS

CHAPTER 1

The Floriculture Industry

CHAPTER 1

The cultivation and selling of flowers is known as floriculture, and those involved in floriculture are called flower growers, producers, or florists. Actually floriculture is one of the branches of agriculture, and it would be perfectly proper to call flower growers "farmers." However, because of the high degree of specialization, their requirements and their methods of doing business are quite different from wheat, corn, or livestock farmers.

- ## FLOWER GROWERS ATTEMPT TO PRODUCE CROPS THE YEAR AROUND

Flowers cannot be preserved or stored for long periods of time as can grains or meats. It is necessary for flowers to be produced continuously throughout the year. In order to do this the grower either seeks the climate that is suitable for growing flowers during all seasons of the year or else he provides a structure that will allow him to make a suitable climate for the plants. In most of the United States it is satisfactory to provide this climate the year around in greenhouses. This is a costly venture, but it can make land productive all year, and it can improve greatly the quantity of flowers that are produced.

- ## SOME AREAS OF THE COUNTRY ARE BETTER FOR FLOWER PRODUCTION

Many greenhouses have been located in a particular area because of the great amount of light during the winter or the mild climate. This accounts for the vast areas in greenhouses in California, Colorado, and a few other locations in the country. This is the reason also for the many hundreds of acres of land in flower crops in Florida—in greenhouses, in slat sheds, under cloth, and in the open. The other

3

most important reason for the location of a greenhouse is nearness to
the market. Thus each town or city has one or more greenhouses
supplying its needs, and the larger cities often attract large greenhouses.

- ## WHOLESALE GROWERS SPECIALIZE AND RETAIL GROWERS RAISE SEVERAL CROPS

Producers of wholesale cut flowers find it more economical to
grow only a few kinds of flowers—many produce only one kind. The
cut flowers that are produced in the greatest quantities are chrysanthemum, rose, and carnation.

Producers of wholesale pot plants often grow several different
kinds of plants as they are sold primarily for the holidays, and each
holiday may require a different selection of plants. Thus a producer
may grow poinsettia for Christmas; lily, hydrangea and azalea for
Easter; geranium for Decoration Day; and chrysanthemum for
Thanksgiving. In addition to this he may produce chrysanthemum,
African violet or gloxinia throughout the year.

The retail grower may attempt to produce as many as possible of
the different types of flowers that he needs for his own shop. This is a
convenience, and in some instances he may be able to produce them
more reasonably than he can purchase them on the wholesale market.
Practically, however, he cannot produce everything that he would like
because of the different conditions and care that the various crops
need.

- ## WHOLESALE CUT FLOWER GROWERS MAY SELL THROUGH COMMISSION HOUSES OR DIRECT

Most cut flowers are sold to the retail flower shops through
wholesale commission houses. These are stores that accept flowers on
consignment from the wholesale flower grower, and they deduct a
commission when the flowers are sold. This commission is around 20%
of the selling price. The wholesale grower bunches and packs his
flowers for the market, and if the commission house is nearby, he
delivers the flowers early each morning. Some growers ship flowers by
air, truck, or rail to several commission houses throughout the country.

Wholesale commission houses are open from about 6:30 A.M. to
3:00 P.M. Some of the retail shop buyers come to the market each day

Fig. 1—1. A wholesale commission house with an ideal arrangement for wholesale selling. The customer can see the stock of flowers through the large windows in the refrigerator. For telephone sales the salesman has full view of the flowers in the refrigerator, and he is constantly aware of the supply. (White Bros. Rose Corp. photograph)

Fig. 1—2. Many wholesale commission houses operate truck routes to neighboring cities making deliveries direct to the flower shops on the route at least twice a week. This truck carries both cut flowers and pot plants.

and select their needs. Many do all of their buying by telephone. Usually the wholesale commission man contacts his customers by telephone several times a week, and he may operate regular truck routes to smaller towns.

Some wholesale growers, in order to maintain better control over their products, have established their own wholesale commission houses. They then attempt to sell all of their own flowers as well as receive some on consignment from other wholesale growers for resale.

Fig. 1—3. A look in the cut flower section of the truck shows the wide assortment of flowers that are brought directly to the flower shop.

Other wholesale growers elect to sell direct to retail shops. They may operate regular truck routes in their area or they may ship direct to the retailer.

Regardless of his method of selling, the wholesale grower must constantly be sure that his flowers are being handled properly, priced

Fig. 1—4. Flowers and accessories sell more readily when they are attractively displayed in the flower shop. (DeSantis Florist photograph)

right, and completely sold. This requires close cooperation between the growers and the sellers. Flowers must be sold within a day or two after they arrive at the market or they are an entire loss to the grower.

● WHOLESALE POT PLANT GROWERS SELL MOST OF THEIR PLANTS DIRECT

Some of the pot plants are sold through the wholesale commission houses, but the larger amount goes directly from the greenhouse to the retailer. In some instances the retailer comes to the greenhouse to make his selection as well as do the hauling. Very often the pot plant grower delivers the plants within a certain distance of his location at no charge.

Some of the growers operate regular truck deliveries providing door to door service to the retailers weekly.

Fig. 1—5. A good retail display refrigerator keeps the flowers in excellent condition and well displayed to promote sales. (DeSantis Florist photograph)

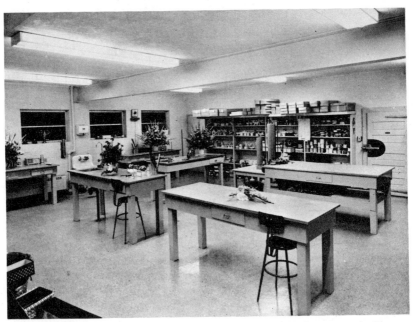

Fig. 1—6. The flower shop work room needs to be well lighted, roomy, and with easy access to the refrigerator and supplies. (DeSantis Florist photograph)

Usually pot plants are produced fairly close to the area in which they are sold because they cannot be shipped or trucked around the country as easily as cut flowers.

- **RETAIL GROWERS SELL MOST OF THEIR FLOWERS IN THEIR OWN SHOPS**

If the retail grower's plans have been right, he will be able to sell most of his flowers at his own shop. This is ideal, for if he does have excesses and attempts to place them on the wholesale market, he often finds that these flowers are also surplus on this market and they are lost or bring a low price.

In many areas the retail florists, the growers, and the wholesale commission people band together in "florists' allied" groups for the common good of the flower industry in that particular area. Several of these allieds have done outstanding work in the promotion of flowers. The allieds work mainly in public relations and advertising. The funds for the operation of the allied group commonly are derived from collecting a small percentage on each transaction that clears through each commission house in the area.

Sending flowers by wire increases the sales of flowers considerably as the customer can send flowers to distant points merely by placing the order with his local florist who then transmits the order by wire to the florist in the city where the delivery is to be made. The customer deals only with his local florist, yet he is able to send flowers with confidence to people in any part of the country. This is possible because organizations like Florists' Telegraph Delivery and Teleflora have florist shop members in all areas. They take care of the wire orders and then report each transaction to the parent organization which handles the payment from one florist to the other.

- **FLOWER GROWERS BUY THEIR PLANTS AND SUPPLIES FROM BROKERS**

Plants, bulbs, and seeds needed by the flower growers come from various sections of the country. Chrysanthemum cuttings are shipped by Yoder Bros., Inc. from Barberton, Ohio or Salinas, California and California-Florida Plant Corp., Fremont, California. Dormant poinsettia stock plants originate from Paul Ecke, Inc., Encinitas, California. Dormant rose plants are produced by a limited number of growers on the West Coast, Arizona, and Texas. Bulbs come from the West Coast and Holland. Carnation cuttings are produced in several areas. Foliage plants are shipped from growers in Florida, Puerto Rico, and California. Seeds originate in California and several other locations. Most of these products move from the specialist producers to the greenhouse flower grower by way of brokers.

The broker very often represents many different plant suppliers. He visits them periodically so that he is acquainted with the stock, and he lists the various items in his catalog. The broker's salesmen call on their flower grower customers several times a year to take their orders. The broker then places the order with the proper supplier of that plant, and shipment is made direct from the supplier to the flower grower.

The flower grower should not only expect to receive good plants through the broker, but also the latest information on how to schedule crops and plan rotations. There are approximately a dozen brokers in the country. Some specialize along certain lines. The following have quite a general line of plants and supplies and publish complete catalogs: Geo. J. Ball, West Chicago, Illinois; Fred C. Gloeckner & Co., Inc., 15 E. 26th Street, New York 10, New York; Jednak Floral Co., Box 1917, Columbus 16, Ohio; and Vaughan's Seed Co., 601 W. Jackson Boulevard, Chicago 6, Illinois.

● **TRAINING IN FLORICULTURE IS AVAILABLE IN HIGH SCHOOLS, VOCATIONAL SCHOOLS, AND COLLEGES**

A few technical or vocational high schools throughout the country have taught floriculture for a number of years. More recently floriculture is one of the subjects offered in vocational agriculture in many high schools.

Training in floriculture above the high school level may be obtained in several schools. These may be one- or two-year courses at vocational schools or colleges leading to certificates or associate degrees upon graduation, or they may be four-year courses or longer for Bachelor of Science or more advanced degrees.

The following table lists many of the institutions in North America which offer instruction in floriculture above the high school level. For possible additional schools that may offer this training, contact the director of vocational education in your state.

The courses referred to in the table should deal specifically with floriculture; however, this may be only greenhouse management or flower store operation or it may be both, depending on the school. Each institution also will offer to floriculture students allied courses of interest such as botany, nursery crops, chemistry, business, and others. Ask the schools, in which you might be interested, to send their catalog or bulletin describing courses or work in floriculture. Whenever it is possible, it is helpful to visit some of the schools to talk to the professors and see the facilities.

INSTITUTIONS IN NORTH AMERICA THAT TEACH FLORICULTURE ABOVE THE HIGH SCHOOL LEVEL[1]

Location	Institution	Number of Courses[2]	Quarter Hours Credit
Alabama	Auburn University[3]	3	16
Arkansas	Arkansas State College	1	6
	Petit Jean Vocational Technical School	3	15
California	California State Polytechnic College, Pomona	4	15
	California State Polytechnic College, San Luis Obispo	7	25
	University of California, Davis[3]	1	2
	City College of San Francisco	6	24
	Fresno State College[3]	1	3
	Los Angeles Pierce College	1	6
	Modesto Junior College	1	6
	Napa Junior College	1	3
	Ventura College	1	6
Canada	University of Alberta[3]	1	6
	Olds Agricultural and Vocational College	2	10
	Ontario Agricultural College[3]	4	30
Colorado	Colorado State University[3]	5	16
Connecticut	University of Connecticut[3]	9	36
Delaware	S. Hallock du Pont School of Applied Science[3]	1	3
Florida	Junior College of Broward County	1	4½
	Daytona Beach Junior College	4	21
	University of Florida[3]	3	15
	North Florida Junior College	1	4
Georgia	University of Georgia[3]	2	8
Hawaii	University of Hawaii[3]	2	9
Illinois	Chicago City College, Woodrow Wilson Campus[3]	2	6
	Danville Junior College	4	17
	Dupage Horticultural School	9	37
	University of Illinois[3]	9	40½
	Southern Illinois University[3]	1	4

(Continued)

INSTITUTIONS IN NORTH AMERICA THAT TEACH FLORICULTURE
ABOVE THE HIGH SCHOOL LEVEL[1]—(Continued)

Location	Institution	Number of Courses[2]	Quarter Hours Credit
Indiana	Purdue University[3]	2½	12
Iowa	Iowa State University[3]	4	12
Kansas	Kansas State University[3]	4	22½
Kentucky	Eastern Kentucky University	2	13
	University of Kentucky[3]	3	13½
Louisiana	Louisiana Polytechnic Institute[3]	1	4
	Louisiana State University[3]	3	9
	Southeastern Louisiana College	3	13½
	University of Southwestern Louisiana[3]	6	18
Maine	University of Maine[3]	2	11½
Maryland	Gaithersburg Vocational School	1	6
	University of Maryland[3]	6	24
Massachusetts	University of Massachusetts[3]	3	16
Michigan	Michigan State University[3]	13	50
Minnesota	Area Vocational and Technical School, Brainerd	2	6
	University of Minnesota[3]	6	18
Mississippi	Mississippi State University[3]	4	25
Missouri	University of Missouri[3]	6	25½
Montana	Montana State University[3]	1	4
New Jersey	Rutgers—The State University[3]	4	12
New Mexico	New Mexico State University[3]	2	6
New York	Cornell University[3]	5	21
	State University of New York Agricultural & Technical Institute, Alfred	24	75
	Agricultural & Technical Institute, Cobleskill	7	24
	Agricultural & Technical Institute, Farmingdale	8	36
	Agricultural & Technical Institute, Morrisville	8	36
North Carolina	Catawba Valley Technical School	2	8
	Forsyth Technical Institute	3	14
	University of North Carolina[3]	5	28
North Dakota	North Dakota State University[3]	1½	4½
	North Dakota School of Forestry	5	36
Oklahoma	Oklahoma State University[3]	2	9
Ohio	Ohio State University[3]	6	30
Oregon	Oregon State University[3]	6	24
Pennsylvania	Pennsylvania State University[3]	6	21
	Temple University[3]	4	18
Rhode Island	Rhode Island State University[3]	7	27
South Carolina	Clemson University[3]	2	6
South Dakota	South Dakota State University[3]	4	15
Tennessee	Tennessee Technical University	2	6
	University of Tennessee[3]	2	6
Texas	Texas A&M University[3]	8	36
Utah	Brigham Young University	2	8

(Continued)

INSTITUTIONS IN NORTH AMERICA THAT TEACH FLORICULTURE
ABOVE THE HIGH SCHOOL LEVEL[1]—(Continued)

Location	Institution	Number of Courses[2]	Quarter Hours Credit
	Utah State University[3]	2	6
Vermont	University of Vermont[3]	2	9
Virginia	Virginia Polytechnic Institute[3]	2	5
Washington	Clover Park Vocational Technical Institute	2	4
	Seattle Community College[3]	3	9
	Washington State University[3]	3	6
West Virginia	West Virginia University[3]	4	15
Wisconsin	Kenosha Technical Institute	5	21
	University of Wisconsin[3]	2	8

[1]These institutions in the calendar year 1966 awarded the following degrees or certificates to graduates majoring in floriculture: Associate or certificate, 299; B.S., 137; M.S., 33; Ph.D., 6.
[2]Floriculture courses are considered to include courses or work in greenhouse cut flower crops, pot plant crops, bedding plants, home gardening, and flower shop management. They do not include such courses as nursery management, garden store operation, identification of landscape plants, and landscaping.
[3]Research in floriculture or extension work in commercial floriculture or both are done as well as teaching in floriculture.

- ## RESEARCH IN FLORICULTURE IS DONE AT U.S.D.A. AND SEVERAL STATE AGRICULTURAL EXPERIMENT STATIONS

The United States Department of Agriculture does research in many phases of floriculture at Beltsville, Maryland, and work with some of the individual crops is done at outlying stations throughout the country. Results of U.S.D.A. research are reported in the trade papers, and copies of these reports can be obtained by writing to the United States Department of Agriculture, Washington, D.C.

Open house for inspection and reports on research work in floriculture at U.S.D.A., Beltsville, Maryland, is scheduled periodically.

The kind and amount of research work done in floriculture at state agricultural experiment stations are related to the size of the industry in the state and the types of crops that are grown. Most of these state experiment stations regularly publish reports of the results of work being done, and they will place you on their mailing lists if you request them to do so. If you do not know the location of the experiment station in your state, an inquiry to the university will be properly referred.

- ## PARTICIPATION IN TRADE ORGANIZATIONS IS HELPFUL

The national trade organization is the Society of American Florists (SAF). Its motto "Say It With Flowers" is familiar to all. The

SAF is headquartered in Washington, D.C., and its primary work is in public relations and publicity. It is the organization that represents the floriculture industry in national legislation and in relation with other industries.

Roses, Inc. is the national organization for greenhouse rose growers. This organization has regional meetings several times a year and a national meeting once a year. A bulletin is published regularly with cultural and promotional information. Roses, Inc. is headquartered at East Lansing, Michigan.

The American Carnation Society has a yearly national meeting and some regional meetings. It is headquartered at 1001 South 54th Street, Philadelphia, Pennsylvania 19143.

Many states have organizations of flower growers or florists. Their activities vary considerably depending on the amount and kind of flower industry in the state. Most states have active retail florists'

Fig. 1—7. Instruction in floriculture at the university gives the student a good understanding of plant growth and development and prepares him for responsible positions in industry. (The Ohio State University photograph)

groups as flower shops are distributed quite evenly over the country. The state flower grower organizations are more active in the states where the production of flowers is large. Many of these state organizations publish bulletins that are excellent sources of information on research in floriculture. You should be a member of your state flower growers' organization, and it is worthwhile to belong to the organizations of some other states just to receive their publications and attend their meetings.

The following flower grower organizations are quite active and regularly publish bulletins of general interest:

California State Florists' Assn., 640 Brannan Street, San Francisco, California

Colorado Flower Growers Assn., Inc., 901 Sherman Street, Denver, Colorado 80203

Illinois State Florists' Assn., University of Illinois, Urbana, Illinois 61803

The Maryland Florist, 1346 Connecticut Avenue N.W., Washington, D.C. 20006

The Michigan State Florists' Assn., 217½ Ann Street, East Lansing, Michigan 48823

New York Flower Growers, Inc., Prattsburg, New York 14873

Ohio Florists' Assn., 1827 Neil Ave., Columbus, Ohio 43210

Pennsylvania Flower Growers, 50 N. Main Street, Chalfont, Pennsylvania

• TRADE PUBLICATIONS ARE PUBLISHED WEEKLY

If you are in the floriculture industry it really is necessary to subscribe to and read one or more of the trade papers. It is here that you get the pertinent news, cultural information, editorial comments, and trade advertising. *The Florists' Review* gives coverage across the country. *The Exchange* gets good distribution in the East and the *Southern Florist & Nurseryman* in the South. These publications may be addressed as follows:

The Exchange, 1199 Broadway, New York, New York 10001

Florists' Review, 343 S. Dearborn Street, Chicago, Illinois 60604

Southern Florist & Nurseryman, 120 St. Louis Avenue, Ft.
Worth, Texas

CHAPTER 2

Structures for Growing Flowers

CHAPTER 2

Some flower crops are produced on open land much the same as are farm crops. Gladiolus is an example. Winter crops are grown in Florida and then progressively farther north until the summer crops are produced in Michigan and other northern states.

Other crops are grown for a short period of the year while the weather conditions are suitable for a particular locality. Delphinium are grown in the North during the summer, stocks* in Arizona and California in the winter, and chrysanthemum in Florida during the winter.

- **FLOWER CROPS NEED GOOD SUNLIGHT, UNIFORM TEMPERATURE, PROPER AMOUNTS OF MOISTURE, AND MODERATE AIR MOVEMENT**

For most of the flower crops it is not possible to find or provide weather conditions outdoors that are consistent enough for continuous production of flowers the year around. Temperature is very critical. Freezing is not the only concern. Most plants grow best within a fairly narrow temperature range, and some may not produce flowers at temperatures that are too low or too high.

Plants need enough water but not too much. They must be in well drained locations and have moisture applied at the proper times. Outdoors we can provide irrigation during the dry periods, but there is little that can be done about heavy downpours other than providing a structure of some kind over the plants. There is an advantage to being able to control the amount of moisture in the air, too.

Some air movement is very good. None at all may encourage disease problems, and excessive winds may cause physical damage to the plants.

---

*A list of the more technical or unfamiliar terms is found in the glossary.

Fig. 2—1. This is a ridge and furrow range in the process of construction. It illustrates the gutter and gutter posts between each house, the roof support trusses at each post, the purlins extending the length of the greenhouse, and the roof bars from ridge to gutter. (Ickes-Braun Glasshouses photograph)

Fig. 2—2. A free span greenhouse showing truss attachment to ridge, purlins, gutter, and eave. (Ickes-Braun Glasshouses photograph)

Any structure that is built for growing flowers needs to allow for the maximum amount of light to enter it during the winter months. In most areas extremely low light conditions exist sometimes during the period from November 15 to February 15.

- ● **THE GREENHOUSE IS THE BEST STRUCTURE FOR GROWING PLANTS**

The minimum amount of framework is used for a greenhouse, and this is covered with glass or plastic. This framework consists of side posts at about 10-foot intervals that support roof trusses. The eave or gutter extends from post to post at the point where the truss joins the side post. The ridge extends from truss to truss at the peak of the house, and midway between the ridge and the eave a purlin extends from truss to truss. If the house is wide, two or more purlins may be spaced equidistant between ridge and eave. For wide houses or for trusses that need additional support, posts are provided at each truss from the purlin to the ground.

The greenhouse structure must be strong enough to support itself, anything attached to it, and a snow and wind load; yet it must be light enough so that sunlight enters easily. Steel can be used successfully. The most serious objection to it is that it rusts easily, and there is considerable maintenance cost in keeping the structure painted. For this reason aluminum is used quite commonly, and many of the newer greenhouses have a completely aluminum framework.

The greenhouse framework is enclosed by placing a curtain wall for 2½ feet to 3 feet around the base of the greenhouse, and then the rest of the framework is glazed with glass or plastic. For glazing with glass, the glass is placed in the roof bars that extend from the ridge to the eave and in the wall bars that extend from the eave to the top of the side wall. The roof and wall bars are spaced to accept the width glass to be used. A common width glass is 24 inches. Bedding compound is placed in the groove of the bar, and starting at the eave, the glass is put in place. Each piece of glass laps the piece below it by about ¼ inch, and it is held in place on wooden bars with glazing nails, and on aluminum bars by clips. A bead of glazing compound is run along each side of the bar, and bar and glazing strip then are painted to complete the seal.

Fig. 2—3. The gutter between two ridge and furrow greenhouses showing gutter post and attachment of roof bars and truss. (Ickes-Braun Glasshouses photograph)

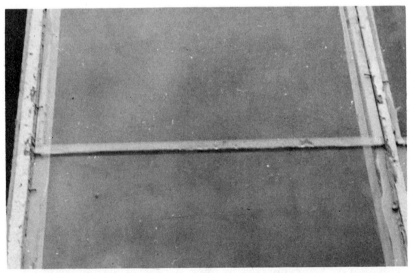

Fig. 2—4. In glazing on wooden bars, nails or glazing points are placed at the bottom edge of the glass to keep it from slipping down and at the top surface to keep the glass tight to the bar. When the glass is in place, a bead of glazing compound is run on both sides of the bar, and then bar and glazing compound are painted to complete the seal.

During the summer there may be more sunlight than needed for the plants, and it may be best to put shading compound on the greenhouse to reduce the light and heat within it. Usually fall rains and frost remove the shading compound before the poor light conditions of winter start, but if not, the greenhouse must be washed and brushed so that as much light as possible can enter it during the winter. The fall is also the time to repair or replace slipped or broken glass, and to make sure that the houses are as tight as possible before cold weather starts.

Fig. 2—5. It is necessary to be able to work on the top sides of greenhouses. Various methods are used. This is a simple ladder that rests on the roof bars and allows the worker to get to all parts of the roof to apply glazing compound or paint.

Moisture often condenses on the under surface of the roof of greenhouses, and the greater the difference in temperature between outdoors and inside, the more moisture there will be. In glass houses the roof bars have grooves along the sides, and the moisture collects and flows down these grooves to the side walls. The drip grooves in roof bars need to be cleaned periodically as they get algae growth on them and become dammed-up. In some instances the algae even grow out over the glass, and the roof then needs to be washed on the inside, too. A well constructed and maintained glass house does not leak or drip.

It is difficult to prevent dripping in houses constructed from film plastic. The moisture collects in droplets on the underside of the film and when the plastic is jarred or rippled, the droplets shower down. There are drips also from the purlins in film plastic houses.

Fig. 2—6. This shows the roof bars and the clip that holds the glass on aluminum roof bars. Note the drip groove in the side of the bars for conducting condensation from the roof to the side wall. (Ickes-Braun Glasshouses photograph)

The moisture on the inside surface of rigid plastic houses flows down the valley of the corrugation, and it will go all the way to the side wall unless it meets an obstruction. Rigid plastic houses should be constructed so that the valleys of the corrugation do not rest on the purlins.

The exterior of the greenhouse needs to be painted about every two years to maintain a good seal between bar and glass. Eventually the glazing compound becomes dry, and the roof will leak. Then the glass must be removed, the bars cleaned, and the house reglazed.

Glazing for aluminum bars is done about the same way as it is on wooden bars, but paint on aluminum houses is used just to complete the seal between bar and glass. Wooden and steel houses must be painted periodically on the exterior to preserve the framework, and paint also increases the amount of reflected light in the greenhouse. Before painting the exterior of the greenhouse, all loose or slipped glass is put in place, and loose glazing compound is removed and a new bead of glazing compound run in its place.

Before painting the interior of the greenhouse, loose paint must be chipped off, corrosion removed from the steel members of the framework, and algae and other dirt cleaned from the wooden bars. There is quite an advantage in co-ordinating the interior painting with the change of crops in the greenhouse. It is much easier to paint an empty greenhouse than one containing plants that can be damaged or are difficult to work around.

Good quality paints must be used in greenhouses as the humid conditions cause rapid deterioration of paint. Some greenhouse paints contain fungicides to reduce the amount of fungus growth on the paint, but these should not be mercury fungicides as roses and some other plants are injured by mercury fumes.

Glazing, painting, and reglazing can be costly, and many growers attempt to reduce or eliminate this cost by using aluminum bar caps or by glazing the greenhouse with plastic. The bar cap is placed over the bar after glazing. It protects the seal between bar and glass, and exterior painting and reglazing may be reduced.

- VARIOUS PLASTIC MATERIALS HAVE BEEN USED
  FOR ENCLOSING GREENHOUSES

The ideal plastic material for covering a greenhouse would have the clarity of glass, would be easily installed, would be inexpensive, and would be suitable for use for several years without replacement. As compared to glass, some plastics have several advantages, but a completely satisfactory substitute for glass is difficult to find. Some of the plastics transmit about 70% to 80% as much light as glass, and this can be a problem in the many areas of the country where winter light conditions are low anyway. In spite of the low light transmission, some good results have been obtained in growing several crops, and it is possible that these results are associated with the type of light that is transmitted by the plastic. The light is diffused as it comes through many of the plastics, and because of this the light rays can hit the plant from all angles, possibly giving the plant as much light despite the lower light intensity.

Film plastics such as polyethylene and vinyl (PVC) are inexpensive and can be installed rapidly, but they must be replaced frequently. If installed in the fall, polyethylene may last through the winter. It deteriorates quite rapidly in bright sunlight, although improved types of polyethylene which last longer are available. The best features of polyethylene are that it is inexpensive and can be obtained in sheets that are wide enough to cover an entire greenhouse. For these reasons, polyethylene has been used for seasonal covering of houses or for temporary structures. In Florida many of the foliage plant stock areas (slat sheds or plastic screen houses) are enclosed with polyethylene in late fall, not only to protect the plants from occasional freezing temperatures, but also to provide better growing temperatures throughout the winter. In the North polyethylene sometimes is used for temporary structures that are in production only during the spring or other portions of the year. In some instances polyethylene has been used to get a production area started; later, when more funds are available, the plastic houses are replaced by glass houses.

Vinyl film is more durable than polyethylene, and the right type of vinyl can be expected to give satisfactory service for a year or even more. Vinyl film may cost about twice as much per square foot as polyethylene. The widest width for vinyl is 6 feet, and this may make the application of vinyl to the framework a bit slower than the wider width polyethylene. However, because of the longer lasting qualities of vinyl film, it is used on year-around structures more successfully than polyethylene.

Mylar polyester film is clearer and more durable than polyethylene or vinyl. It can be expected to last longer than one year—possibly several years. The cost of Mylar approaches the price of glass, but the installation cost is less. Mylar is available in widths up to 52 inches.

The framework for plastic film houses is usually entirely wooden

Fig. 2—7. A film plastic house for growing azaleas in Alabama. (Blackwell Nurseries photograph)

Fig. 2—8. A film plastic house for growing year around crops in the North. (Stylon, Inc., photograph)

and made from regular stock lumber as this is considered to be the most inexpensive framework for a temporary structure. Wood preservatives should be used on the lumber, but it is necessary to be sure that they do not harm either the plants or the plastic. The fumes from some common wood preservatives are toxic to plants, and in general petroleum-base materials should not be used on plastics.

Designs vary considerably. In Florida the flat-topped, foliage plant slat sheds have been replaced with peaked-roof structures that can be covered with polyethylene in order to shed water. These are post type buildings that are covered with plastic screen the year around; the film plastic is placed over the top just for the winter.

In California large areas were covered with saw-tooth type wooden structures covered with polyethylene and used primarily for the production of cut flowers.

In the North various types of framework are used for plastic houses. Usually they are separate houses about 20 feet wide with "A" frames and rafters about 4 feet apart. If rafters are spaced farther apart, wire fabric is placed over the framework to give support to the plastic film. Some metal frame, quonset type structures are available. These are covered with a single piece of polyethylene held in place with tie ropes over the structure at each rafter.

Film plastic can be applied to the framework either lengthwise to the structure or across it, depending on how the width of the plastic fits on the framework. As vinyl and Mylar are made only in rather narrow widths, it is best to apply them lengthwise on the structure. Polyethylene may be available in wide enough widths to cover the entire width of the house with one piece. Before constructing the framework, the plan for covering it should be well in mind so that the structure will provide the necessary support and the rafters will be at the right spacing for the width of material that is to be used.

● SOME RIGID PLASTICS ARE USED FOR COVERING GREENHOUSES

Fiberglass is a plastic product that is made of imbedded glass fibers in plastic resin. It is easily installed, but it is not nearly as clear as glass. The plastic erodes gradually, and periodic surface applications of acrylic resin are needed or the glass fibers become exposed; dust and dirt then remain on the surface and further reduce the light.

There is also some color change in fiberglass after a few months' use. The initial cost of fiberglass is greater than glass, but the installation costs are less.

Rigid PVC (rigid vinyl) was introduced as a covering for greenhouses more recently than fiberglass. Various formulations are available and some "clear" types are really quite muddy. However, there are some clear PVC products that approach the clarity of glass—and apparently they retain this clarity. Rigid PVC is handled in about the same way as fiberglass, and since it is clearer and less expensive, PVC will be used if it gives the same length service.

Rigid PVC and fiberglass come in rather narrow widths, and it is therefore best to apply these materials to ridge, purlins and eave, rather than to rafters or roof bars. The structure for the rigid plastics should have purlins every two feet to three feet the width of the house, depending on the thickness of the plastic and the pitch of the

Fig. 2—9. This shows the inner surface of a corrugated rigid plastic house. Spacers are used in attaching the rigid plastic to the purlins so that the condensation flowing down the inner surface of the roof will be able to flow all the way to the side walls.

roof. Since these materials are corrugated, it is necessary to use plastic closure strips at the eave and ridge. The corrugated plastic is put on the roof with the corrugations running in the same direction as the pitch of the roof so that the water runs freely from the roof. Rigid plastic is fastened to the purlins with screw-nails or screws. Holes are drilled in the peak of the corrugation slightly larger than the nail or screw to allow for expansion and contraction, and spacers are used between the peak of the plastic and the purlin so that the valley of the corrugation does not touch the purlin. Any condensation on the inside surface of the plastic will run down the valley of the corrugation, and if this rests on the purlins, the water will drip from the purlins instead of flowing all the way to the side wall.

- ### VENTILATORS OR EXHAUST FANS ARE USED FOR AIR EXCHANGE IN THE GREENHOUSES

It is necessary to provide a good means of exchanging the greenhouse air with outdoor air in order to regulate the greenhouse temperature, adjust the humidity, provide air movement around the plants, and introduce new supplies of oxygen and carbon dioxide. Traditionally, greenhouses have ventilators at the ridge, and separate greenhouses usually have ventilators at the eaves as well. The ventilators can be opened or closed as needed to adjust the temperature in the greenhouse. If the ventilators are operated by hand, the grower must be aware constantly of the greenhouse temperature and the need for adjustment of the ventilators. Power equipment can be installed on ventilators so that they are operated by a motor that is activated by thermostat. Such equipment requires an outlay of capital, but it releases labor for other jobs and makes it possible to do a more uniform job of ventilation than with manual operation. The ventilators need to be operated so that the temperature is regulated properly, and there is some circulation of air but no cold drafts directly on the plants. The ventilator on the side away from the direction of the wind should be used as this will provide an exchange of air without rapid changes in temperature.

Some greenhouses are constructed without ventilators, and ventilation is handled by exhaust fans. During the summer the exhaust fans are used to draw air through moistened wood-fiber pads on the

Fig. 2—10. The ventilators at the ridge and in the side walls provide a means for regulating temperature, air moisture, and air movement in the greenhouse. (Ickes-Braun Glasshouses photograph)

Fig. 2—11. Operating mechanism for ridge ventilators. (Ickes-Braun Glasshouses photograph)

Fig. 2—12. This greenhouse range covers approximately 8 acres of ground. The office and workroom are located between the two greenhouse areas. The boiler room is on a railroad spur to the north of the greenhouses. Most of the greenhouses are separate houses, and they are connected with a wide, covered walk. Two of the greenhouses appear white as they have been sprayed with shading compound to reduce the temperature inside for camellias. (White Bros. Rose Corp. photograph)

opposite wall of the greenhouse. This system provides some air cooling as well as air circulation. In the winter the moist pad is removed and the wall is closed except for an opening for one or more perforated polyethylene tubes. As the exhaust fans remove the air from the greenhouse, the air from outdoors enters the perforated tubes and disperses evenly throughout the greenhouse. The exhaust fans can be operated by thermostats, making this ventilating system automated. Exhaust fan ventilation can provide good ventilation and an exchange of air throughout the year, and in many instances they have replaced the traditional greenhouse ventilators.

• SIZE AND ARRANGEMENT OF GREENHOUSES

Before the type of greenhouse is chosen and built, a careful study should be made of the best bench arrangement in the house for the crops that are to be grown, then choose the greenhouse that will best accommodate this arrangement. Too often the greenhouse is erected first, and then the benches are fit in as best they can be. Sketch the benches and walks, and try to visualize how the work will be done in the house. Be sure that the walks are wide enough for sprayers or carts. If a greenhouse with purlin posts is going to be used, make certain that the posts will not interfere with planting, shading, or sterilizing the benches. Crops such as roses need a lot of head room, and houses with at least 7-foot walls should be used. Generally, it is better to have a number of smaller houses for pot plants than a single large house since this makes it easier to provide the different temperature areas that are needed for timing the pot plant crops for the holidays. Cut flower crops can be grown conveniently in larger houses; however, there is an advantage in having "crop size" houses as the temperature can then be adjusted to the stage of growth of the crop. There is an advantage in finishing some cut flower crops cool, but this cannot be done if there are young plants in the same house with plants in flower.

The relationship of one greenhouse with another and the relationship of the greenhouses with other work areas need to be considered. Usually the most economical use of ground area is to build connected or ridge and furrow greenhouses. Construction may be a bit cheaper, too, than with separate greenhouses. The disadvantages of connected houses are that the entire area must be operated at the same temperature unless walls or partitions are used between the houses, the houses must be connected with gutters to carry away the water from the roofs, and these gutters cast shade on the crops on that side of the house.

Separate houses may have side ventilators as well as those on the ridge, and this can be quite an advantage in ventilating them. If separate houses are used, they need to be connected by covered walks so that the workers can go from house to house without going outdoors. If the houses are 200 feet long or longer, the connecting walk usually is placed at the middle of the greenhouse in order to

Fig. 2—13. A combination of plastic houses, glass houses, lath houses, and outdoor growing for this azalea production area in Alabama. (Blackwell Nurseries photograph)

minimize the distance to be traveled from any part of the greenhouse to the center walk. Shorter greenhouses may have the connecting walk along the ends of the houses.

Any type greenhouse needs to be located conveniently to the other work areas. Pot plant greenhouses must be adjacent to both the potting room and the shipping room. It is a big help to have a shipping area for pot plants that is big enough for wrapping and staging the orders and then loading directly onto trucks. It is difficult to load trucks directly from the greenhouse. The orders cannot be grouped for loading properly, and the loading depends on suitable outdoor weather. It may be almost impossible to load in cold or inclement weather.

Customers of pot plants like to inspect the holiday plants and make some of their own selections. This is true whether the plants are being sold wholesale or retail. Be sure that the greenhouses where the plants are finished are convenient places for the customers to make their selections. Take particular care to see that the walks are in good condition, and that there are no obstacles in the way of the customers.

Cut flower greenhouses should be located so that the flowers can be moved efficiently to the flower grading area and from there to the refrigerators. From the refrigerators the flowers are packed and then loaded on trucks. The packing and shipping room should therefore be convenient to the refrigerators.

Boiler rooms should be as centrally located as possible so that the minimum lengths of mains and returns are needed between the greenhouses and the boiler. All of the buildings should be so located that they do not shade the greenhouses. If they can be placed to the north of the greenhouses, shading is no problem. If they cannot be placed to the north of the greenhouses, the buildings must be at sufficient distance that they do not cast shade on the plants.

Greenhouses should be located and constructed so that the plants will get the best possible light during the winter. There is less shading from the roof bars in greenhouses that are placed in an east-west direction. At one time, uneven-span greenhouses were located on south slopes of hills with the long span to the south. This may have had some advantage in the amount of light in the greenhouse, but it is difficult to work houses that are built on hills. Greenhouses do need to be located so that the maximum amount of light can be obtained, but a generally level area should be chosen so that wheeled vehicles can be used.

● GREENHOUSE BENCHES

The requirements of greenhouse benches are to provide nearly level but freely draining units that can be sterilized efficiently, not be recontaminated, and be the right height and width for working with the crop. For convenience in working, cut flower benches are often slightly elevated from the ground and are 3½ feet to 4 feet wide. This gives sufficient head room for the plants to grow, and the bench is not too wide for the flowers at the middle of the bench to be supported and cut properly. Pot plant benches are raised higher and are usually wider as pot plants can be worked on benches up to 8 feet in width. The best height is 2½ feet for pot plant benches.

Fig. 2—14. Concrete ground benches. Note that the welded wire support fabric is placed directly on the soil for planting. It is raised as the plants grow.

Benches must be built almost level, and the soil in them must also be level or it will not be possible to water the soil properly. If the benches are not level, water will run to the low side of the soil, leaving the high side dry and the low side constantly wet.

If the bench is built directly on the ground, it should be made from concrete so that it can be completely sealed-off from the surrounding soil. Solid-bottomed concrete benches should have V-bottoms for good drainage, and the whole bench should be slightly pitched from one end to the other so that it will drain.

Raised benches may have solid V-bottoms and drain from one end, or they may have flat bottoms with drainage slots placed frequently enough along the length of the bench to provide good drainage. If the bench is made of wood, the bottom boards are spaced so that there are drainage cracks between boards. Wood expands when it is wet, and care must be taken to allow enough space between boards so that there still is a space after the bench is watered. Flat-bottomed concrete benches are poured with drainage slots in the bottom. With benches made from corrugated transite, it is best to pitch the bottom slightly from one side to the other, and then allow a sufficient drainage space at the low side. If this is not done with transite, holes must be drilled in the valleys of the corrugations to provide drainage.

Fig. 2—15. Bench bottom for pot plants made from 1″ x 1″ welded wire fabric. This allows perfect drainage and excellent air circulation around the plants.

Bottoms for pot plant benches must be level and must drain freely, too. One of the best materials for pot plant bench bottoms is 1 inch by 1 inch welded wire fabric. This provides excellent air movement around the plants as well as perfect drainage.

The depth of a bench for cut flowers needs to be at least 6 inches, and in most instances it would be better to have a depth of 7 inches or 8 inches. With pot plants it is not necessary to have side boards on the bench, as this allows better air circulation around the plants.

Traditionally, benches have been placed lengthwise in the greenhouse. One of the primary reasons for this has been the method of installing heating lines. If the heating lines are on or under the benches, the benches just about have to be placed lengthwise in the house. If overhead heating units are used, the benches can be placed for the best working arrangement without concern for the heating system. In some situations it is better to place the benches across the house rather than lengthwise. This can be particularly helpful in pot plant houses as wheeled carts can be used in the walk along the bench ends and this eliminates the necessity for carrying plants by hand the length of the greenhouse. With some cut flower crops, cross-benching may provide better size units for planting and cutting.

Fig. 2—16. Cross-benching in the greenhouse, with an end walk wide enough for wheeled carts, speeds the work in some houses.

Walks between benches occupy about one third of the space in a greenhouse. They should be as narrow as possible and yet allow the work to proceed unhampered. Usually there is one wide walk in a house—wide enough for sprayers, wheelbarrows, or wheeled carts. This is the center walk in a house benched lengthwise, and it is the side walk in houses benched crosswise. Walks need to be kept serviceable. A rough or sloppy walk slows the work. It actually saves time to keep the walks in good condition.

- **THE HEATING SYSTEM IN THE GREENHOUSE**
  IS STEAM OR HOT WATER

Each system has advantages. Larger and more pipes are needed for hot water systems as the temperature of the water is not as high as that of steam. Temperatures can be kept more uniform with hot water, but hot water systems also may be slower to heat and slower to cool than steam systems. State regulations vary on the operation of steam boilers, but usually operators of steam boilers must be licensed. Steam systems require more supervision and more maintenance than hot water. Very often small greenhouse ranges have hot water systems, while large greenhouse areas are heated with steam.

An important consideration is the availability of steam for steam sterilization of soil. Some hot water systems can be converted to steam just for sterilization purposes. If the hot water system cannot be used for steam sterilization, a steam generator should be obtained just for sterilizing soil and equipment.

Steam systems produce steam in their boilers and the steam is piped to the various greenhouses in mains. Low pressure steam systems operate at less than 15 pounds per square inch steam pressure. High pressure systems may produce steam at 90 pounds or more per square inch. The pressure is reduced to about 5 pounds before entering the greenhouse. Steam mains and heating lines are pitched slightly up. That allows the water that condenses in the lines to flow back toward the boiler until it picks up sufficient heat to change to steam again. Mains and heating lines must be hung so that they can expand and contract with changes in temperature. Expansion loops or joints need to be built into the lines to provide for this expansion. Steam traps are placed in mains and lines where condensation can be expected to collect. The traps pass water through them but not steam, and they feed into lines that return the water to the boiler. Some steam systems operate entirely by gravity. The boiler is in a pit, and the hot, light steam rises up through the mains and heating lines. The water returns to the boiler room in lines that are pitched toward it from the greenhouses. Many systems, however, depend on pumps to return the water to the boiler room, in which case the boiler can be on the same level as the greenhouses. Hot water systems can also operate as gravity systems, but many of them use circulation pumps that speed the flow of hot water to the greenhouses or the return of water to the boiler.

The "radiators" in greenhouses are usually pipes that extend the length of the greenhouse. Commonly there are some pipes hung on the side walls and other pipes on the sides of or under the benches. In some instances, all of the heating lines are placed overhead except for some side lines on the side walls. Overhead lines are not practical with hot water as the number of pipes needed would create considerable shade. Overhead steam lines can be an advantage as they are more easily installed and replaced; they do not corrode as rapidly; and the heating results can be just as good as with bottom lines. A further improvement with overhead systems is using air circulation fans in conjunction with them to assure good air circulation and even distribution of heat throughout the greenhouse.

The amount of heating lines required in a greenhouse is determined by computing the amount of heat loss from the house. To figure the heat loss from a greenhouse, it is necessary to know the square foot area in the roof, sides, and ends of the greenhouse as well as the temperature to be maintained inside at a given low temperature outdoors. To determine the heat loss from a greenhouse that covers an area 25 feet by 100 feet, that will be maintained at 60° inside at 0° outdoors, and is attached to a work building that will be maintained at 60°, it is necessary to know the height of the side walls, the length of the roof bars, the height of the ridge above the eave, and the height of the curtain wall around the base of the greenhouse. This house has 7 foot side walls, the lower 2 feet of which are concrete and the remainder glass. The roof bars are 14 feet long, and the distance from the eave height to the ridge is 6½ feet.

```
2,800  sq. ft. roof (28 x 100)
1,000  sq. ft. glass side walls (5 x 200)
  200  sq. ft. glass equivalent of concrete side walls (2 x 200 x ½)
  125  sq. ft. glass end wall (5 x 25)
   25  sq. ft. glass equivalent of concrete end wall (2 x 25 x ½)
   81  sq. ft. glass gable (6½ x 25 x ½)
-----
4,231  sq. ft. total
```

The heat loss from concrete or wood is considered to be one half that from glass so only one half of the concrete wall area is used to

Fig. 2—17. Steam heating lines on the side wall.

Fig. 2—18. An overhead steam heating coil used with the Nivola Dutch Mill air circulation fan. Such systems can produce excellent heating and reduce steam line maintenance. (Eddyco, Inc., photograph)

give the equivalent of that area in glass. A simplified method of finding the area of the gable end of the greenhouse above the eave is to multiply the width times the height of the ridge above the eave and take one half this value. In this example, only one end of the greenhouse was included as the other end butted onto a 60° building and there would be no heat loss there. The coefficient of heat transfer through glass is 1.13, so the total square feet of glass area or equivalent is multiplied by 1.13 and then by the temperature difference (60°) between inside and out, and this gives the heat loss per hour from the greenhouse in B.T.U. The heat loss from the greenhouse in this example would be about 286,862 B.T.U. per hour.

With a water temperature of 180° and a greenhouse air temperature of 60°, 1 linear foot of 2-inch pipe will give off heat at the rate of about 160 B.T.U. per hour. With steam pressure of 5 pounds per square inch and a greenhouse temperature of 60°, 1 linear foot of 1¼-inch pipe will give off heat at the rate of about 180 B.T.U. per hour. If the 25-foot by 100-foot house in the example is to be heated with hot water, it would require about 1800 linear feet of 2-inch hot water pipe or eighteen lines of pipe the length of the greenhouse. If the heating system is steam, about 1600 linear feet of 1¼-inch steam pipe would be required or sixteen lines of pipe the length of the greenhouse.

If this greenhouse is to be heated with unit heaters instead of pipe, the heat output of the heaters must be known. With hot water at 180° and unit heaters rated at 70,000 B.T.U. per heater, if three unit heaters were used in the greenhouse there would be a deficit of about 80,000 B.T.U. to be made up with five 2-inch lines the length of the greenhouse. If three steam unit heaters are used that are rated at 70,000 B.T.U. each, the deficit could be supplied with five 1¼-inch lines the length of the greenhouse. When the primary source of heat in the greenhouse is overhead, some heating lines low on each side of the house should be supplied in addition to the overhead supply.

During the heating season it is necessary to operate the heating lines and the ventilators in such a way that the proper temperatures are maintained constantly, good air circulation and exchange are provided, and the air moisture is kept in a suitable range. On sunny days all of the objects in the greenhouse become heated by the sun's

Fig. 2—19. Steam traps allow water to pass through but not steam. The water is returned to the boiler. Note that a union is used in the line just before the trap so that the trap can be removed easily for inspection or repair.

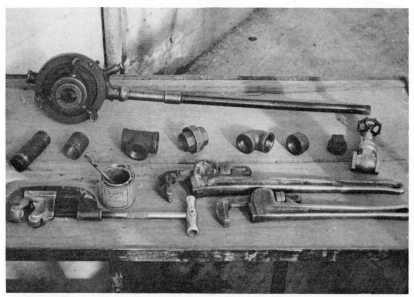

Fig. 2—20. A pipe thread cutter at the top, and at the bottom left to right, pipe cutter, pipe dope, and pipe wrenches. At the center left to right, nipple, coupling, tee, union, ell, cap, plug, and gate valve.

rays and reradiate the heat to the surroundings. Even on very cold days outside, it may not be necessary to operate the boilers if the sun is bright; however, as the sun wanes in the afternoon, heat must be provided from the heating lines. The best plan is to pick up the temperature in the greenhouse in the afternoon with the heating lines before the sun goes down and continue to vent. In the morning, continue to use the heating lines until the sun picks up the temperature. The correct air temperature should be maintained, but slightly more ventilation is used during this transition from natural heating to artificial heating.

One of the reasons for making sure that the heat source is actually present is that solid objects like plants cool more readily than the surrounding air when a heat source is removed. In such a situation, moisture from the warm air deposits on the cool leaves or flowers, and this allows diseases to get their start. The film of moisture on the plant may be so slight that you cannot see it, but it can still be sufficient to start the germination of disease spores.

Some heating systems operate automatically from thermostats, and all that may need to be done is to make sure that the setting is right on the thermostat and to operate the ventilators correctly. If the heating system is manual, the grower will need to turn lines on or off as needed. For best results the lines that are on should be evenly distributed over the house, and only the minimum number of lines should be on. This provides more uniform temperatures throughout the house.

If a steam line is turned on but is not heating, this usually means that the trap is not discharging water and needs to be repaired or replaced. If a hot water line is on but not heating, that can mean there is an air block and the line needs to be vented.

● **GREENHOUSE COOLING**

During the summer the temperatures are often too high for the best plant growth. Greenhouses can be cooled by evaporating moisture in them, and this is done by drawing the air through moistened pads or by injecting fine, high-pressure mist into the air. As the moisture evaporates, heat is removed from the surroundings. It is possible to reduce the greenhouse temperature 10° to 20° during the

Fig. 2—21. Exhaust fans installed in the side wall of the greenhouse for pad and fan air cooling system. Note that the ridge ventilators are closed during the operation of this system. (Acme Engineering & Mfg. Corp. photograph)

Fig. 2—22. Wood fiber pad installed in the side wall of the greenhouse for pad and fan cooling system. Note that the ridge ventilators are closed during the operation of this system so that all of the air enters through the moist, wood fiber pad. (Acme Engineering & Mfg. Corp. photograph)

summer, and this is sufficient to make an improvement in the quality of the plant growth.

With pad and fan cooling systems, exhaust fans are placed in one greenhouse wall and porous wood fiber pads are installed in the opposite wall. Water is trickled over the pad. The fans exhaust the air in the greenhouse, and the only opening for air to enter is through the moist pads. As the moisture from the pads evaporates, heat is taken from the surroundings and the temperature in the greenhouse is reduced. During the night the exhaust fans may be used for air circulation and ventilation, but the water for the pads is shut off as the night air is usually too humid during the summer anyway.

Mist systems for cooling must provide mist that is fine enough to evaporate without any fall-out of water on the plants. This requires a

Fig. 2—23. Gable end ventilators and framework for the installation of a wood fiber pad for pad and fan cooling system. (Ickes-Braun Glasshouses photograph)

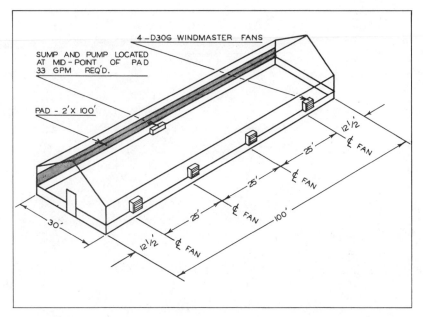

Fig. 2—24. Pad and fan installation on the side walls of the greenhouse. (Acme Engineering & Mfg. Corp. photograph)

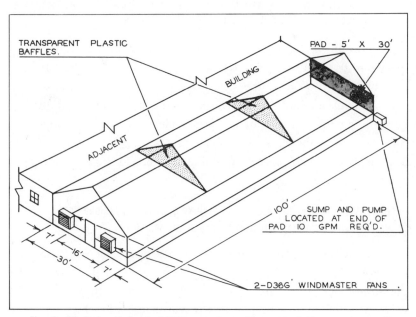

Fig. 2—25. Pad and fan installation on the gable ends of the greenhouse. (Acme Engineering & Mfg. Corp. photograph)

Fig. 2—26. The Mann Hi-Pressure Mist System provides air cooling during the summer and humidity control at any time of the year. (E. G. Hill Co., Inc., photograph)

water pressure of 500 pounds per square inch or higher, with nozzles spaced regularly throughout the greenhouse. A good high pressure mist system will provide the same degree of cooling as pad and fan systems; and, in addition, they can be used at any time of the year to raise the humidity of the air in the greenhouse. This is an important consideration as the air in the greenhouse can be very dry during the heating season, and a means of adding moisture to the air can benefit plant growth.

- COLD FRAMES ARE VERY OFTEN USED FOR STORING DORMANT PLANTS DURING THE WINTER AND FOR STARTING SOME PLANTS IN THE SPRING

The sides of the frames are made of boards or concrete block, and they are 1 to 2 feet high, depending on the height of the plants to be placed in them. Cold frames are made 6 feet wide so that they can be covered easily with the standard glass sash that is 3 feet by 6 feet. The rear wall of the frame is built higher so that water will drain from the

Fig. 2—27. The cold frame provides additional area for starting plants in the spring or for holding plants in the fall. The frame is covered by 3' x 6' glass sash that can be lifted or removed for ventilation and temperature control.

Fig. 2—28. Philodendron pertusum totem poles being grown in a slat shed in Florida.

Fig. 2—29. The exterior of a plastic screen house for growing chrysanthemum or azalea in Florida.

Fig. 2—30. In central Florida the foliage stock plants are grown in slat sheds or plastic screen houses. Most of the plants are propagated in heavily shaded greenhouses. During the winter the plastic screen houses are covered with polyethylene film, and they are heated with steam. (Evergreen Gardens of Apopka, Inc., photograph)

sash. Cold frames are inexpensive to construct, but they require considerable labor to operate.

Lath houses, slat sheds, and cloth houses are sometimes used as growing structures during the summer in the North, and the year around in warmer climates such as Florida, California, and Puerto Rico. Lath or slat sheds usually are constructed to provide from 50% to 75% shade. They are used in the North to grow crops such as hydrangeas and azaleas during the summer. In Florida and Puerto Rico they are used for growing various foliage plants the year around. Cloth houses are made with cotton, tobacco cloth or plastic screen fabric. They provide about 50% shade, and in the North they are used for growing summer crops of mums, aster, and snapdragons. In the warmer climates they may be used for growing several different crops at any time of the year.

CHAPTER 3

How the Surroundings Affect
Plant Growth

CHAPTER 3

Plants are living things, and when they are placed in the right surroundings they will grow. There are several different types of plants, but the ones that are used for flower production in greenhouses are green plants that have roots, stems, and leaves. These are known as vegetative parts.

● ROOTS, STEMS, AND LEAVES MAY VARY ON DIFFERENT PLANTS

The roots usually grow in the ground, but some plants such as orchids have aerial roots as well. Many plants have fine, fibrous roots, but some such as the dahlia have coarse, fleshy roots.

Quite often stems are thought of as being above ground only, but there are many types of underground stems, too. These are special stem structures such as bulbs (lily), corms (gladiolus), and rhizomes (German iris). The above-ground stems may vary, too, from the woody canes of roses to the soft and succulent stems of snapdragons or the thick stems of cacti.

Leaves can vary in many ways. A leaf may have a broad blade and a narrow petiole such as the chrysanthemum, or the blade may be long and attached directly to the stem (sessile) such as the carnation. Rose leaves are compound—each leaf consists of three or five leaflets.

● GREENHOUSE PLANTS EVENTUALLY FORM FLOWERS
  AND POSSIBLY SEEDS AND FRUITS

This is known as reproductive growth as it is a means of sexual reproduction of the plant. Depending on the type of plant, flowering terminates growth of the entire plant or that portion of the plant where the flower is located. New vegetative growth, followed by reproductive growth, will then have to come from vegetative buds below the flower. It is possible to get succeeding flower crops from plants, and such plants as carnations are cropped for one or two years and roses for three or four years. Continuous cropping could be done with chrysanthemums and snapdragons, but it is more economical to discard the plants after each crop and start new plants.

Fig. 3—1. A chrysanthemum stem that has formed new growth since planting and is at the right stage of growth for pinching.

• PLANTS ARE MADE UP OF CELLS, AND GROWTH OF PLANTS RESULTS FROM THE INCREASE IN NUMBER OF CELLS AND IN THE ENLARGEMENT OF THESE CELLS

   Cells increase in number by division. Increase in length results from the increase in the number of cells by division at the tips of the plant—stem tip and root tip. Cell division takes place right at the tip and enlargement of these cells occurs immediately in back of the tip. Increase in width (diameter) of stem is caused by the formation of new food-conducting cells (phloem) and new water conducting cells (xylem). The arrangement of the phloem and xylem varies in different types of plants, but the results that are most familiar are the rings in tree trunks. These rings are actually the xylem that is formed each

Fig. 3—2. In making the pinch just the very tip of the plant is removed. This is the stem shown in Fig. 3-1 after the pinch.

year, and by counting the rings the age of the tree can be determined. These rings vary in width from year to year, and this is directly related to growing conditions—during droughts the annual ring is narrow.

Stems grow in length if the surroundings are favorable, and stem and leaves are formed until this growth in length is terminated with a flower. When this occurs, new shoots start in growth from leaf buds located at the point where the leaf attaches to the stem (leaf axil). In many instances it is desired to have more than one stem per plant, and

Fig. 3—3. After pinching shoots form at the leaf axils below the pinch.

Fig. 3—4. The effect of pinching is approximately the same on all types of plants. Here are azalea stems that have been pinched, and new shoots are forming in the axils of the leaves in the same manner as in chrysanthemum.

Fig. 3—5. The chrysanthemum shoots continue to grow forming a branched plant.

Fig. 3—6. If the plant is growing well at the time of the pinch and if the pinch is made in the new growth, the leaves immediately below the pinch enlarge greatly. The shoots that arise from the axils of these leaves are strong and heavy.

this is accomplished by removing (pinching) the tip of the stem when the plant is young. The leaf buds below the pinch, then grow forming a branched plant.

Root growth takes place in much the same way as stem growth. The increase in root length is due to the formation of new cells at the tip and the enlargement of these cells. Increase in diameter is related primarily to formation of phloem and xylem cells. Growth in length in roots does not terminate however. It is a continual process. Just in back of the growing tip are the fine root hairs that are the main absorption area for roots. They are short lived, and continuous root growth in length is needed for a continuous supply of root hairs. Side branching of roots does take place, and these branches arise from tissues of the inner root. Branching of roots is good, for it provides more growing tips and thus more root hairs with added absorption area.

• FLOWER BUDS FORM IN STEM TIP WITH RIGHT CONDITIONS

Usually the start of formation of a flower in a stem tip is not noticed until it is rather far advanced and there is a flower bud present. The flower bud, however, was preceded by a change in cell formation in the stem tip—leaf type cells no longer were formed and in their place flower type cells were initiated. If conditions are favorable, the flower type cells are formed until the complete but rudimentary flower is present in the bud. Depending on conditions, the flower bud may continue to develop to full maturity or may remain as a tight bud until more favorable conditions are present.

One set of conditions may be needed for the formation (initiation) of the flower bud, and another set needed for the development of the flower bud to the flowering stage. These conditions often are either temperature or day length or a combination of the two.

• PLANTS CAN SPORT TO NEW TYPES OR VARIETIES

Sometimes differences are noticed in growth in only a portion of a plant—this may be in flower color or size or shape, or it may be in length of flower stem, variegation of leaves, or other characteristics. This is known as mutation or sporting, and the change usually originates with a single cell in the plant. Mutation is an important

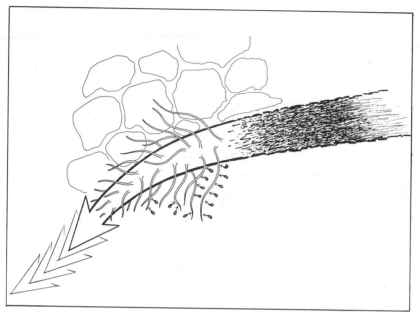

Fig. 3—7. Root growth needs to be continuous as it is in the root hair area immediately in back of the root tip that water enters the plant. Without continuous new root growth the water absorption area for the plant is reduced. Root growth is better in coarse, porous soils.

Fig. 3—8. Root growth and top growth are directly related. It is not possible to have good top growth with a poor root system. Here are lily bulbs started at the same time and showing the effect of poor root growth on the top.

source of new, improved types of plants. Since plants can be propagated vegetatively, these mutations or sports can be increased endlessly.

Practically all of the carnation varieties that are grown are sports from one variety, William Sim. It is a red carnation, but by means of mutation or sporting it gave rise to white, pink, yellow, and variegated

Fig. 3—9. If the chrysanthemum is in the proper day length and temperature, flower buds will be formed at the stem tip and to the side below it.

carnations in a period of a few years. The color change is the most obvious difference, but these sports from parent William Sim also vary from the parent in some instances in stem length, stem diameter, flower size, flower fragrance, splitting, size of leaf, number of flowers produced, and other characteristics. The Sim "family" of carnations is a classic example among greenhouse plants of mutation. However, mutation occurs in all kinds of plants, and the greenhouse operators should be looking constantly for new, improved types of plants and flowers.

• THE TRANSPORTATION SYSTEM OF PLANTS IS LIQUID

Water is transported mainly through the xylem, and dissolved foods through the phloem. Generally there is little lateral movement

Fig. 3—10. In many instances the lateral flower buds in the chrysanthemum are removed leaving a single terminal flower bud per stem.

of water or food in the plant. The roots on one side of the plant are in connection with the stem and leaves on that side of the plant. Effects on roots in one area should be expected to be noticed on the stem and leaves directly above that area.

• PLANTS CONTAIN PIGMENTS AND HORMONES

Possibly the best known pigment is the one that gives plants their green color—chlorophyll. This pigment is involved in the very important food manufacturing process in plants. Other pigments produce different leaf and flower colors.

Plant hormones are growth substances that may influence the formation of roots, shoot development, and the enlargement of cells. They are present in very tiny amounts in the plant, but they can cause considerable difference in the reaction of the plant. It is hormones that cause roots to grow downward and shoots upward.

- **GREEN PLANTS HAVE THE WONDERFUL ABILITY TO MANUFACTURE FOOD**

This is called photosynthesis. The plants do need to be green, because the pigment, chlorophyll, must be present for photosynthesis to take place. If plants are in a sufficient amount of light and enough carbon dioxide and water are present, food (sugar) can be made. This food manufacturing process takes place primarily in the leaves, and the food then is distributed throughout the plants in the phloem. This food is very necessary for good growth and development of the plants. This is the food from which new cells are made, and it is this food that makes plant growth possible. Since the place of food manufacture is in the leaves, it is important to develop and maintain good-sized leaves on the plants. With some plants, like roses, the leaves shed readily in unfavorable conditions, and this reduces the area in which food can be manufactured.

- **PHOTOSYNTHESIS CAN TAKE PLACE MOST EFFICIENTLY IN MANY GREENHOUSE PLANTS WHEN THE LIGHT INTENSITY IS ABOUT 6,000 FOOT CANDLES**

Since the light intensity on summer days may be in excess of 10,000 foot candles, plants may grow as well or better if they are placed in partial shade at that time. In the greenhouse, plants are shaded by spraying a shading compound on the outside of the glass or by placing muslin, tobacco cloth, or plastic screen above the plants inside the greenhouse. A combination of the two types of shade may be used in some instances. Plants grown in too strong sunlight typically have short, heavy stems; small, light-colored leaves; and bleached flower colors. With the right amount of shade during the summer the stems will be longer, the leaves larger, and the color of leaves and flowers deeper.

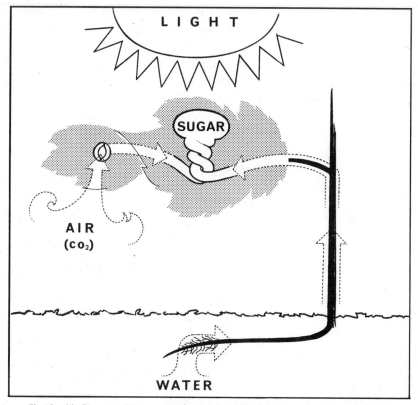

Fig. 3—11. The manufacture of sugar (photosynthesis) takes place in green plants in the light if sufficient supplies of water and carbon dioxide are available. It is this sugar that supplies energy and growth of the plant.

Stems of plants bend toward the source of light. This is caused by the greater enlargement of the cells of the plant on the shady side of the stem.

Light also affects the pigment in plants. In most plants the green chlorophyll does not develop until the plant is in the light. In excessive light both leaf and flower color may be bleached. With chrysanthemums, during the summer, light muslin cloth is often suspended over the plants as they come in flower to prevent the fading of the flower colors by the strong light.

In some areas, in the winter, the light may not be above 500 foot candles for several days at a time, and the day length is shorter than in summer, as well. Food production in the plants is seriously reduced under such conditions, and this has a bad effect on the quality and quantity of flowers that are produced. Every means should be taken to furnish the maximum amount of light to plants during the winter. If possible, plants are spaced farther apart during this period to reduce the shading of one plant by another, and of course overhead obstacles should be removed and the glass cleaned. In some instances artificial light can be used for growing plants experimentally, but there is no economical means of furnishing enough light by artificial means commercially to promote photosynthesis.

- **THE CARBON DIOXIDE SUPPLY MAY BE LOW AT CERTAIN TIMES OF THE YEAR**

It is possible that the greenhouse air during the winter may have less than the normal .03% of carbon dioxide, and this might limit the amount of photosynthesis. To conserve heat in cold weather the ventilators may not be opened for long periods of time, and as a result there is little exchange of air with the outside. The glass in cold weather may be frosted too, sealing the laps between the glass, further reducing the exchange of air with the exterior. During such periods the carbon dioxide concentration inside the greenhouse may be considerably below that of outdoors. Since carbon dioxide is one of the ingredients used in photosynthesis to make food, there could be times during winter days when the supply of carbon dioxide in the greenhouse air is so low that it limits photosynthesis. Some improvement in plant growth may be made by increasing the air circulation so that the air in the immediate vicinity of the leaves is constantly changed, or by adding carbon dioxide to the air in the greenhouse. This can be done by the use of organic mulches or by injecting CO_2 into the greenhouse directly from dry ice or from CO_2 generators.

Carbon dioxide is given off by decaying organic matter and mulches thus serve the additional purpose of being a source of supply of carbon dioxide in the greenhouse. Mulching, however, is not practical on every crop—in fact, roses are really the only crop that commonly are mulched. Most mulches decay rather rapidly, and to be an effective source of carbon dioxide a mulch would probably have to be applied every four to six weeks. Certainly mulching is worthy of consideration as it would not only supply some CO_2, but it also would help condition the soil.

Dry ice converters are the simplest system for adding carbon dioxide directly to the greenhouse atmosphere. Two dry ice converters of 150 pound capacity are required for each area to be serviced, together with pressure regulating valves, pressure gauge, and a perforated plastic tube for distributing the gas around the area. The converters must be charged with dry ice periodically, and the rate of flow of gas is adjusted so that the desired amount of carbon dioxide is released into the greenhouse air. Air circulation fans used in conjunction with this system are beneficial as they not only assure uniform distribution of carbon dioxide throughout the entire air mass, but they continually bring a new air supply in contact with the leaves.

Carbon dioxide generators develop CO_2 by burning either propane or natural gas. They have the potential of furnishing CO_2 at a lower cost per pound, but there are more equipment costs involved with this system.

Carbon dioxide is injected into the greenhouse air only during the daylight hours as photosynthesis occurs only when the plants are in light. Since sunlight is low in most parts of the country during the winter, this also limits photosynthesis. The beneficial response from adding CO_2 can be expected to be greatest in the areas of the country where the winter light conditions are good. Usually the attempt is to add enough CO_2 to maintain a concentration of .05% or more during the day. Carbon dioxide can be added to the greenhouse atmosphere effectively only when the ventilators are closed. In most areas of the country that limits its use to the period from November to May.

The effects of CO_2 injection are not the same on every crop. The growth cycle is fast for roses, and it appears that more beneficial results might be apparent on roses during the winter because the growth can be made during the injection period. By comparison, carnations grow slowly and much of the growth for the winter crop is made before it is possible to inject CO_2 in the fall. Carbon dioxide injection in the greenhouse atmosphere can be useful with some crops in some areas, but careful trials are necessary first to determine the exact manner in which it can be used to good advantage.

Because of the injection of CO_2 or the manner in which it is used, some adjustments in growing procedures may be necessary. Temperatures are commonly run higher during the day. This allows a longer period with closed ventilators and consequently a longer period for the injection of CO_2. Crops generally will have to be irrigated more frequently and fertilized more heavily.

● SOME PLANTS RESPOND TO THE LENGTH OF DAY (PHOTOPERIOD)

This effect can be very dramatic as it may cause flowering, leaf drop, tuber formation, or fall color, but the effect on flowering is of the most interest for greenhouse plants. The chrysanthemum normally flowers in the fall during short days, and the year around flowering of chrysanthemums is made possible by making days short or long artificially to promote either leafy growth or flowers as desired. Day length control also is used with the poinsettia, which is commonly given a few artificially long days in the fall to delay flowering until Christmas. Many kinds of plants are apparently unaffected by photoperiod.

Very low intensity light is needed to increase the photoperiod. The amount varies with different plants, but it may be as low as 1 foot candle. Electric lights are used to extend the day length, and black cloth is placed over the plants to provide short days. Usually a minimum of 10 foot candles of light is furnished in extending the day length, and it is best to add this light around midnight so that the dark period is not longer than seven hours. When black cloth is used to provide short days artificially, it is placed over the plants for at least twelve hours each day—usually from 7 P.M. to 7 A.M.

● LIGHT, TEMPERATURE, AND HUMIDITY ARE
   DIRECTLY RELATED

The more sunlight there is, the higher the temperature will be in the greenhouse. As the temperature rises, however, humidity will decrease. Irrigation will need to be more frequent, and misting or other means of adding moisture to the air may also be required.

During the heating season, the grower must be very temperature conscious. In the daytime the sun is the primary source of heat on clear days, and in spite of cold temperatures outdoors, no additional heat may be needed inside the greenhouse—in fact, the ventilators may have to be raised to reduce the temperature on bright winter days. A rapid temperature drop occurs, however, when the sun disappears behind a cloud during cold weather, and it requires fast action to close ventilators and turn on steam lines to prevent harmful temperature fluctuation in the greenhouse. The good operator will learn to anticipate the need for ventilation or heat, and he will be ready to make the changes as needed. This by no means implies that the temperatures should be run a bit on the high side, just in case a temperature drop comes along. Too high temperatures can be as bad for the plants as too low temperatures.

- ### TEMPERATURE EFFECTS ON PLANTS ARE GREAT, AND PARTICULAR ATTENTION IS PAID TO NIGHT TEMPERATURES IN THE GREENHOUSE

In fact, the plants are usually classed by night temperatures. Day temperatures are 5° to 10° warmer depending on whether the sky is cloudy or sunny.

Generally plant growth is faster at warmer temperatures, but the quality of growth may not be so good. Stems may be longer but not as heavy. Flowers may be smaller and the color bleached or faded. The common night temperatures in the greenhouse are 50° for such crops as carnations and snapdragons, and 60° for roses, chrysanthemums, and poinsettias. Warmer temperatures are used for foliage plants or for propagation of plants, and cooler temperatures are used for holding plants dormant or for developing and maturing flower buds on some plants.

Some plants form and develop flowers over a wide range of temperatures; however, chrysanthemum and azalea require about 60° minimum temperature. After the bud is well developed, the azalea requires a cool storage period below 50° for the bud to mature. The hydrangea also requires a cool storage period after the flower bud is developed, and most of the bulbs need cool storage or other special temperature treatment so they will flower satisfactorily after being brought into the greenhouse. For early season forcing, plants are stored at 45° as that is cool enough for the cool temperature effect, and the plants force faster than when stored at cooler temperatures.

For long term storage or for plants that are going to be forced later in the season, temperature just above freezing may be used.

● TEMPERATURE AND ITS RELATION TO DISEASES AND PESTS

The influence of temperature on diseases may be a direct effect on the rate of growth of the disease organism, but in many instances it is the indirect effect of temperature on the air or soil moisture and thereby on the growth of the disease organism. The rose grower must be sure that he maintains good air circulation and avoids sudden temperature changes. A slight deposit of water vapor on the leaves is sufficient for the start of a serious infestation of powdery mildew.

Water vapor may be deposited on rose leaves mainly in two different situations: during humid conditions, when there is little air movement (this is primarily in the summer); and during times when the leaf cools more rapidly than the surrounding air (this is primarily in the heating season when the source of heat fluctuates). Maximum ventilation should be used in high humidity, and air circulation fans will also help. During the heating season, failure is associated most commonly with lack of steam heat as the sun disappears and reappears. In the afternoon the steam lines should be operated so that the daytime temperature of 70° is maintained until the sun is down, and then the steam heat should be reduced as needed to adjust the air temperature to the nighttime temperature of 60°. In the morning the air temperature should be brought up to the daytime temperature of 65° or 70° with steam heat and then the steam reduced only when the sun is sufficiently high to maintain that temperature. Two difficult times of the year are fall and spring when temperatures are on the borderline, and there is a question if the steam system should be operated or not. In many instances the decision to operate the boilers is based on an outdoor temperature of 60°. The decision probably should be based on an outdoor temperature of 70°. Heating expenses would be increased, but the incidence of powdery mildew on the roses should be reduced.

When the temperatures drop in the fall, soils dry more slowly. If the watering practices are not changed accordingly, the poinsettias are very likely to contract either Rhizoctonia or Pythium or both, as these two organisms thrive in soils that are constantly moist.

Generally, insect pests are more active and multiply more rapidly at warmer temperatures. This is one of the reasons why pests are more of a problem during the summer. Careless operators who allow their houses to go up to 80° or 90° during the daytime in winter can also expect increased numbers of pests.

• TEMPERATURE DIFFERENTIAL PRODUCES AIR MOVEMENT

Heated air is lighter and rises. It is possible to get air circulation in the greenhouse by doing some heating while having the ventilators partly open. This may seem wasteful of heat, but it does perform the good service of reducing the humidity, evening the temperature throughout the greenhouse, and introducing new air. If air circulation fans are not used, the difference in temperature between the indoor and outdoor air is really the only means of providing air circulation in the greenhouse.

• SOIL AND AIR MOISTURE HAVE IMPORTANT EFFECTS ON THE GROWTH OF PLANTS

Very often only soil moisture is considered in discussing moisture for plants. Air moisture (humidity) is also very important. Unfortunately, quite often it is difficult to adjust air moisture as needed. High pressure mist is a good method of adding water vapor to the air when it is needed. The mist must be so fine that it evaporates into the greenhouse air rapidly without any fallout as moisture on the plants. This requires water pressures of 500 pounds per square inch or more. When a high pressure mist system is activated with humidistats, the air moisture can be adjusted as needed. Since evaporating water takes heat from the surrounding air, the high pressure mist system also is an effective means of cooling the air during the summer. About 10° to 20° cooling can be expected from using a good high pressure mist system on a hot summer day. Other than that, about the only thing that can be done is to keep the surroundings (such as walks and the area under benches) moist and gain air moisture by evaporation. This is a help, but it really is not effective.

The greenhouse air is usually too dry during the day during the summer, and it is even drier both day and night during the heating season because the heated air rises and deposits moisture on the under side of the glass. The colder it is outdoors, the more moisture will be deposited on the glass and the drier the air inside will be.

During the non-heating season the night air is very often too humid. About the only means of correcting this is to provide maximum ventilation and give the best air circulation possible.

Growth of plants in excessively humid conditions is too soft, as the cells enlarge more than is desirable in the over-abundance of air moisture. Several kinds of disease organisms grow better in moist conditions, and the soft, succulent plants are very susceptible to disease.

In dry air the water loss from the plant (transpiration) may be greater than the water absorption. Cell enlargement will not be as great, and the plants will be shorter, the flowers and leaves smaller, and rate of growth slower.

Water enters the plant primarily through the roots in the root hair area just in back of the root tip. If the root is not constantly growing in length there may be no root hairs present—and thus no entry-way for water into the plant. The good grower constantly inspects the roots to make sure that he is providing the conditions that encourage continual root growth. Plants have a liquid transportation system. It is by means of water that nutrients get to various parts of the plant, and it is by water that the food manufactured in photosynthesis is transported around the plant.

Water is one of the basic ingredients that the plant uses to make food in the process of photosynthesis. A continual, adequate supply of water is needed for both respiration and transpiration to be carried on in the plant.

Since water enters the plant primarily through the roots, it is necessary to have an adequate water supply in the soil. However, only enough water should be provided to assure the best root growth. Root growth of many plants is very poor in soils that are kept constantly wet. Actually the upper portions of plants that are grown in constantly wet soils and in very dry soils may look quite similar—short growth, small leaves and flowers, and poor color. Both plants are suffering from lack of water in the plants. In one case the water is available but there is so much that the roots have been damaged, and the water is not taken into the plant. In the other case the roots are in good condition and water could be absorbed, but there is a deficiency of water in the soil.

- ● THE TWO INGREDIENTS OF AIR OF PRIMARY IMPORTANCE
  TO PLANTS ARE OXYGEN AND CARBON DIOXIDE

Plants use oxygen in much the same way that animals do—to burn food, and this results in energy that is used in growth. Carbon dioxide is one of the materials that plants use in making food in the process of photosynthesis. Air enters the plant primarily through the pores (stomates) of the leaves. Respiration can take place in plants night and day, but photosynthesis, because it is dependent on light, occurs only during the day.

There is an apparently limitless supply of oxygen and carbon dioxide in the outdoor atmosphere, and it is most likely that plants growing outdoors always have a sufficient amount of both for respiration and photosynthesis. A greenhouse, however, can be closed for extended periods during the winter, and it is known that carbon dioxide can be deficient at times and the manufacture of food limited somewhat because of it. The addition of carbon dioxide to the greenhouse air during such periods can promote growth. The CO^2 is added only during the daylight hours when the houses are kept closed, and in some instances the concentration of CO^2 is raised to two or three times as great as the normal amount in the air.

Commonly only the air above ground is considered, but the soil air is also very important. Roots need oxygen for the process of respiration. Without it the roots will not grow and eventually will die. The air supply in coarse, porous soils is good, and this allows good root growth. Fine soils pack tightly, and the air supply in such a soil is inadequate. Generally soils should be watered heavily and then allowed to dry somewhat before being given another heavy watering. This provides both the water and the air that is needed.

Continuous air movement in the greenhouse is good. This is accomplished best with air circulation fans. Continuous air movement provides more uniform temperature and humidity conditions throughout the greenhouse and thus promotes more uniform plant growth and less disease.

Fig· 3—12. Research in floriculture takes place at several universities and agricultural experiment stations throughout the country. Here the results of the use of growth regulant chemicals on chrysanthemums are being evaluated. (The Ohio State University photograph)

Fig. 3—13. Growth regulant chemicals are used by flower growers to regulate the height of some plants and to promote flowering in others. Cycocel can be used to limit the height on poinsettias and to promote earlier formation of flower buds on azaleas. B-Nine is used to limit the height on chrysanthemum, poinsettia, hydrangea, and some bedding plants, and to promote earlier formation of flower buds on azaleas. Phosfon can be used to regulate the height of pot chrysanthemums. (Jednak Floral Co. photograph)

Fig. 3—14. The earlier formation of flower buds on azalea and the formation of multiple flower buds are promoted with the use of either B-Nine or Cycocel.

- **SOME GROWTH REGULANT CHEMICALS ARE USED
  WITH FLOWER CROPS**

Some greenhouse plants grow too tall under ordinary circumstances. Several chrysanthemum varieties grow too tall to make suitable pot plants; poinsettias that are propagated too early make finished plants that are too tall; and some hydrangea varieties are not as short as desired. Either B-Nine or Phosfon can be used to regulate the growth of pot mums. Cycocel or B-Nine will reduce the height of poinsettias, and B-Nine can be used to shorten hydrangeas.

Fig. 3—15. Height regulation with pot chrysanthemums by the use of B-Nine. (Naugatuck Chemical photograph)

Some chrysanthemum cut flower varieties elongate more than desired at some times of the year producing a "necky" appearance below the flower. B-Nine can be used to reduce this elongation.

With some plants the growth regulant chemicals limit stem growth and promote the formation of flower buds. Cycocel and B-Nine are used to produce earlier formation of flower buds and the formation of more flower buds on azaleas.

The use of growth regulant chemicals can be a very useful tool, and it is likely their use will expand as new materials are introduced.

CHAPTER 4

Soils, Fertilizers, and Irrigation

CHAPTER 4

Greenhouse soils must provide good growing conditions for the roots so that the plant is well supplied with water and fertilizer. For continuous root growth the air supply in the soil must be good. This is accomplished best in soils that drain freely of water. Greenhouse benches, beds, and pots must be constructed so that water drains away rapidly and completely, and the soil itself must drain freely. The greenhouse soil should be coarse and porous.

- ## COARSE ORGANIC MATTER OR AGGREGATE IS NEEDED IN GREENHOUSE SOILS

Of all types of soil, gravel is the coarsest and drains the best, and actually excellent plants can be grown in the greenhouse in gravel. However, it requires close attention to watering and supplying fertilizer as gravel does not retain a reserve supply of either water or fertilizer. It is best to use a soil mixture that drains well but still retains some moisture. A good soil mixture can be made by adding organic matter, such as peat moss, straw, strawy manure, or peanut hulls to soil. The organic matter can improve the soil in two ways. As it decomposes it forms substances that can absorb fertilizers and thus provides a more even supply in the soil. This is known as a buffering effect. If the organic matter that is added is coarse enough, it will improve the drainage of water through the soil.

The amount and kind of organic matter to be added to a soil depends on the type of soil that is used. Clay soils are made up of the finest soil particles, and they require the addition of a particularly coarse material to assure good drainage.

- ## CLAY SOILS REQUIRE LARGE AMOUNTS OF COARSE MATTER TO MAKE THEM POROUS

The addition of an aggregate such as coarse gravel or haydite

Fig. 4—1. This is an example of good potting soil made up of soil, poultry litter peat, peanut hulls, and perlite. A coarse soil mixture like this will remain porous and will drain well. A shredder should not be used on soil as that pulverizes it too finely and promotes poor drainage. Note that the pot is not completely filled with soil. About one-half the width of the pot lip of freeboard is needed to allow for enough water to be put on at a time for complete wetting of all the soil in the pot.

may improve drainage in clay soils even more than organic matter. The aggregate, however, must be coarse—¼ inch or more. The addition of finer aggregate or sand to clay is of no benefit. The primary problem with clay soils is drainage, and anything that will help them drain faster and dry more readily will help root growth.

The addition of organic matter to sandy soils is best because it can improve the buffering effect of a sandy soil as well as improve the drainage.

Field soils vary, and the amount of organic matter or aggregate to be added should be adjusted accordingly. Many soils will require at least one fourth organic matter or aggregate by volume.

Greenhouse soils should not be shredded as it pulverizes them, and this increases the water drainage problem. Most mechanical tillers also beat the soil too finely. Hand spading of greenhouse soils is recommended. Organic matter to be added to the soil should not be shredded either, and the poultry litter grade of peat moss is the best type of peat to use as it is coarser.

• ADD SUPERPHOSPHATE AND CALCIUM FERTILIZERS TO THE SOIL MIXTURE

Field soils contain very little fertilizer, and it is best to add phosphorous fertilizer at the time of mixing the soil. Add superphosphate at the rate of 5 pounds per 100 square feet of soil. Some adjustment also may need to be made to soil pH. Most greenhouse plants grow best in slightly acid soil—about pH 6.5. To acid soils add hydrated lime or finely ground agricultural limestone at the rate of 5 pounds per 100 square feet. To alkaline soils add ferrous (iron) sulfate at the rate of 1 pound per 100 square feet.

If neither hydrated lime nor agricultural limestone is needed to adjust the soil pH, gypsum (calcium sulfate) should be added at the rate of 5 pounds per 100 square feet of soil. Gypsum supplies the calcium needed by the plants without affecting the pH of the soil.

Some special soil mixtures are used in the greenhouse. Azaleas are very often grown in peat moss only. In some areas of the country it has become popular to grow a wide variety of plants in mixtures of peat and sand or peat and perlite. These may have the advantage of being a uniform mixture each time, but they do require more attention in fertilizer applications and watering.

• THE SOIL MUST BE PERFECTLY LEVEL AND ABOUT AN INCH BELOW TOP OF BENCH

If the bench is empty and being filled with soil, make sure that the bench bottom is in good condition and that there are sufficient provisions for the drainage of water from the bench. Wooden bench bottoms made from dry wood will be water tight unless about ¼ inch cracks are left between the boards, because wood swells when it gets wet. Older benches may have sagged portions that would develop water pockets if not repaired, and drainage slots in bench bottoms may be plugged. Make sure that the drainage tile in the bottom of concrete, V-bottom benches is in good condition. If the soil is in the bench and is just going to be cultivated and then replanted, cultivate deeply enough to be sure that there is no hard pan of soil at the bottom of the bench. Also investigate the bench bottom enough to make sure that the drainage of water from the bench will not be hampered by plugged holes or slots.

Be sure that the soil in the bench is level from end to end as well as across the bench. If the soil is not level the water will run to the low spots, making it impossible to water the bench uniformly. The low spots on the bench will remain too wet and the high spots too dry, with the result that plant growth will not be uniform. The distribution of fertilizer will also be just as uneven, and this further exaggerates the problem of erratic growth of the plants.

There must be enough freeboard on the bench so that water can be applied rapidly to the soil but still not run over the side of the bench. About an inch of bench side above the soil is sufficient freeboard to contain the water being applied to the soil. A bench that is filled with soil to the top of the side boards just cannot have enough water applied to it at a time to percolate through the entire mass of soil.

- **GREENHOUSE SOILS SHOULD BE STEAM STERILIZED BEFORE BEING USED**

This can eliminate disease organisms, soil pests, and weeds. In addition, it makes the soil more porous and thus improves drainage. Before steam sterilization was in common usage, bench soils were replaced each year with new field soil. Now it is common practice to steam sterilize before each planting, and continue to use the same soil year after year. Since organic matter in the soil does decompose, a new supply of organic matter should be added to the soil each time before sterilizing. Some greenhouse soils have been used successfully for twenty years or longer simply because proper attention was given to the addition of a new supply of organic matter each year, and the soils were carefully steam sterilized before each planting.

Fig. 4-2. The soil in the bench must be coarse so that it drains well. Straw or strawy-manure is an excellent material to mix with soil to improve drainage. The surface of the soil must be level so that water flows evenly over it, and there must be a freeboard space of at least an inch from the soil surface to the top of the side board so that the soil can be thoroughly irrigated without run-off.

Fig. 4—3. Rose soils are mulched with corn cobs, straw, or strawy manure. This is particularly important with rose soils as the plants stay in the same soil for four years, and the mulch keeps the soil in good condition.

Soils can be sterilized chemically; however, steam is better if it is available. The method used is to inject steam into the soil, making sure that all parts of the treated area are held at 180° for one half hour. Moist soils conduct steam best, so dry soils should be uniformly moistened before steaming. Bench soils are steamed right in the bench where they are going to be used. Any organic matter or fertilizer to be added is cultivated in with the soil before steaming and steam conductors are placed in or on the soil. Various types of conductors are used. The object is to provide a perforated channel for distributing the steam evenly the length of the bench. If agricultural tile or perforated pipe is used, it is buried in the soil. If porous canvas hose is used, it is placed on the surface of the soil. Two conductors the length of the bench should be used for benches that are 4 feet wide. Three-foot benches can be handled with one conductor. The steam should be piped into the conductor every 50 feet. Longer distances can be run, but it takes too long to bring all the soil up to the desired temperature.

The entire bench is covered with a plastic cover to confine the steam. Usually vinyl covers are used as they are light and easily handled, contain the steam well, are not expensive, and can stand contact with steam pipes. Polyethylene covers are less expensive, but they are not satisfactory as they disintegrate on contact with steam pipes. As the steam is introduced the cover billows. If the flow of steam is regulated just right, it is possible to maintain the billow without fastening the edge of the cover. If there is any question about being able to control the flow of steam, the cover should be weighted or fastened at the edges as a steam blow-out can burn crops in adjacent benches.

It is important to make sure that the bench bottom is uniformly open, so that the air can escape from the bench as the steam enters. If some of the drainage holes in the bench bottom are plugged or if there is a hard-pan at the bench bottom, the steam will not flow through all of the soil and some areas of the bench will not be sterilized.

Take readings with soil thermometers at various locations in the bench to make sure that all parts of the soil reach 180° and that this temperature is maintained there for a minimum of one half hour.

Fig. 4—4. Vinyl plastic sterilizing cover being placed over a bench before steam sterilization. The porous canvas hose placed the length of the bench conducts the steam evenly throughout the bench, and vinyl plastic cover contains the steam on the bench. (Stylon, Inc., photograph)

Soil for pot plants is sterilized in a chest or in a truck box that is fitted for that purpose. The conductor pipes for such steaming should be no farther than 12 inches apart and the holes in the pipe spaced every 12 inches. Be sure to provide a way for the air to escape as the steam enters the chest.

The steaming job must be thorough. Pots, flats, tools, and all handling equipment must be sterilized also.

Steam should be used for sterilization whenever possible; however, if steam is not available, chemicals can be used effectively in some situations. The chemicals are either liquids that turn to gas or they are in the gas form initially, and it is the gas that infiltrates the soil and gives the fumigation or sterilization. Soil temperatures need to be 50° or above for active fumigation: the soil should be cultivated and moist; and the soil must be covered to keep the gas sealed in. Several chemicals do a good job of sterilizing the soil. The disadvantages are that they cannot be used around crop plants, and the soil cannot be used for planting for two or three weeks after treatment. The most common materials used for chemical sterilization of the soil are methyl bromide (MC-2), chloropicrin (teargas), and Vapam.

• GREENHOUSE PLANTS NEED A CONTINUOUS SUPPLY OF FERTILIZERS

In addition to the sugar that the plant manufactures in the leaves, the plant needs other materials in order to develop and grow properly. Some vital parts of the plant are made from protein, and protein cannot be made in the plant unless it has some nitrogen, sulfur, and probably phosphorus as well as sugar. These materials, dissolved in water, enter the plant through the roots; they are called fertilizers. Many different kinds of fertilizers are needed by plants—some in large amounts and some in very tiny amounts. Soils normally contain some of these fertilizers, but usually with greenhouse crops the required fertilizers must be added regularly to the soil to assure the best growth of the plants.

Organic matter (plants or animals or their refuse) can be used as a source of fertilizer. Some of the animal materials that are used as fertilizers are manure, dried blood, tankage (steamed refuse from slaughter houses), and sludge (treated sewage). Cottonseed meal and tobacco stems are plant materials that are sometimes used as fertilizers. These organic fertilizers break down rather slowly in the soil and release the water-soluble fertilizer materials needed by the plants.

Inorganic matter (salts or chemical materials) can be used to supply the fertilizer needs of plants, and in most instances they are easier to use, are more readily obtained, and are less expensive.

The amount of nitrogen, phosphorus, and potassium that fertilizers contain, must be declared on the label and this is called the analysis. A fertilizer with the analysis of 5-10-5 contains 5% nitrogen, 10% phosphorus, and 5% potassium. A 25-5-20 fertilizer contains 25% nitrogen, 5% phosphorus and 20% potassium. In spite of the fact that the analysis declares only the nitrogen, phosphorus, and potassium content of the fertilizer, many other minerals are present in the fertilizer that are beneficial to the plant. Some of the common materials present in fertilizers are calcium, magnesium, sulfur, and iron. It is very necessary to know what fertilizer materials the soil needs, and then apply the correct amount of the right fertilizer.

There are so many different brands and analyses of fertilizers that they can cause confusion. Since greenhouse soils are reused many times and have a good supply of phosphorus, a fertilizer that is low in phosphorus should be used for regular applications. For dry applications this would be an analysis such as 10-4-6, and for liquid applications an analysis such as 25-5-20.

Fig. 4—5. Read the label on the fertilizer bag. It will always give the analysis of the fertilizer, and very often recommendations for its use are made. Be sure that the right kind and the right amount of fertilizer are used.

- **FERTILIZER APPLICATIONS SHOULD BE BASED ON THE RESULTS OF SOIL TESTS**

After a great deal of experience, it may be possible to know when some fertilizers are needed just by looking at the plant; however, it is always better to make an actual soil test and base the fertilizer applications on the results of the test. If you do not know of a soil testing service, your state flower growers' organization or state university will be able to advise you. Soil tests must be made often enough so that it is certain that the soil contains the right amount of fertilizer at all times. This means testing once a month or possibly more often. If detailed soil tests cannot be made as often as they should be or as quickly as they need to be, it is possible to base fertilizer applications on the results of Solubridge tests made on the soil. The Solubridge will not indicate what kinds of fertilizers are present or what are needed, but it does indicate the total amount of fertilizer that is present in the soil. If the Solubridge indicates that there is a great quantity of fertilizer present, it is then clear that more fertilizer should not be added. If the Solubridge reading is low, some benefit could be expected from a fertilizer application.

Some laboratories have facilities for making tissue tests on plants to determine the status of fertilizer materials in them. This procedure requires quite a bit of time, but it does give a report on conditions that exist in the plant tissues.

Often there is the temptation when the top portions of the plant do not look good, to assume that the soil needs an application of fertilizer. In many instances the poor top growth is the result of an over-supply of fertilizer in the soil, and another application of fertilizer will only further aggravate the condition. Roots grow very poorly and may even be killed entirely if there is too much fertilizer in the soil. Of course, if the root system is not active on the plant, there will be no way for water or fertilizer to enter the plant, and the growth of the top of the plant will not be good.

Root growth can be excellent in soils that have a very low supply of fertilizers. Keep constantly looking at the roots. If the roots are growing actively and the top of the plant is not, it is quite likely that an application of fertilizer will help. If the roots of the plant are not growing actively, the top growth of the plant will be poor regardless of fertilizer until new, active root growth is started.

• APPLY FERTILIZERS IN DRY OR LIQUID FORM

Fertilizers are applied to the soil in different ways. Phosphorus or calcium fertilizers are incorporated into the soil before planting. There is an advantage in doing this as these fertilizers are not highly soluble and it is better to have them mixed uniformly throughout the soil. Superphosphate is used as the source of phosphorus, and it is applied at the rate of 5 pounds per 100 square feet. It is common practice to add superphosphate to the soil each time before planting; however, if the same soil is used for a few years in the greenhouse, the applications of superphosphate can be discontinued as the phosphorus will be sufficient.

Calcium fertilizers are incorporated in the soil for two reasons—to provide some calcium for the plants and to make the soils more alkaline. Hydrated lime or finely ground limestone is applied at the rate of 5 pounds per 100 square feet to make the soil more alkaline. Several applications may be needed on clay soils to adjust the pH, but on sandy soils one or two applications may be sufficient. If the pH of the soil is suitable, gypsum (calcium sulfate or land plaster) is used at the rate of 5 pounds per 100 square feet. It furnishes the calcium that is needed with little effect on the acidity of the soil.

Other fertilizers usually are not incorporated into the soil before planting as too much fertilizer can limit root growth, but some of the slowly available fertilizers could be incorporated without harm. One of several of the organic fertilizers can be added before planting, and specially prepared or coated fertilizers can be used also. Some resin-coated fertilizers have been used successfully as slowly available fertilizers. Some fertilizer seeps through the resin coating as water is applied to the soil, and it requires about three months for the entire supply of fertilizer to be expended.

After planting, fertilizers may be applied in either the dry or the liquid form. The fertilizers for dry application usually are not entirely water soluble, and they have a fairly low analysis such as 10-4-6. Fertilizers for liquid application of course must be water soluble, and they have a high analysis such as 25-5-20. Equally good results can be obtained with either type of fertilizer depending on how it is used.

It is easy to observe that the total declared analysis for a typical dry fertilizer is only 20%, whereas the total declared analysis for a typical liquid fertilizer is about 60%. It is important to know that in most dry fertilizers there is a high percentage of calcium and magnesium included in the bag, but in the fertilizers for liquid application there usually will be none. If all the fertilizer is applied in liquid form, it is very essential to apply calcium fertilizers to the soil as it is mixed before planting.

For pot plants there is little choice. Fertilizers in the liquid form are much easier to apply, and it is possible to make a uniform application readily. For bench crops, some labor is saved by using fertilizers in the liquid form, but a dry fertilizer application is not quite the problem that it is with pot plant crops. As is true with pot plants, it also is easier to make a uniform application of fertilizer to bench crops with fertilizer in the liquid form than in the dry form. There is probably very little difference in rate of uptake by the plant whether the fertilizer was applied in the somewhat insoluble, dry form or in the completely soluble, liquid form as the liquid fertilizer becomes partly insoluble when it contacts some of the minerals commonly found in the soil.

The soil must be moist at the time of fertilizer application, and the fertilizer then is watered in thoroughly after it is distributed on the soil. The applications should be based on soil tests; however, depending on size of plants, kind of weather, and method of irrigation, fertilizer may need to be applied every two to four weeks.

There are primarily three methods that are used for making liquid applications of fertilizer—by use of pump, siphon, or injector. With the pump method the fertilizer is dissolved in water in a large tank, and the fertilizer solution is then pumped from the tank to wherever it is to be used. Fertilizer of an analysis of about 25-5-20 is used at the rate of about 3 pounds per 100 gallons of water, and this solution is applied to the soil at the rate of 1 quart per square foot (100 gallons is applied to 400 square feet). The soil must be moist before applying the fertilizer, but a liquid application of fertilizer does not need to be watered-in. Actually this is using fertilizer at the same proportion as the dry application, and the frequency of application would need to be the same.

Siphon nozzles operate with a suction tube in a container of fertilizer concentrate, and some of the concentrate is drawn into the water stream as the water passes through the nozzle. Siphon nozzles may have different proportions and the proportion may vary with the rate of water flow, but a common one is 1 to 15—for every 15 gallons

Fig. 4—6. A simple faucet attachment for the application of fertilizer in the liquid form. Such a device does reduce the flow of water, but it can be used satisfactorily for watering pot plants. The fertilizer concentrate is drawn from the can through the small tube, and it mixes with the water as it passes through the nozzle.

of water that passes through the nozzle, 1 gallon of fertilizer concentrate is taken up. With such siphons the fertilizer concentrate is made up about sixteen times more concentrated than solutions that are to be pumped directly on the soil. This would be using a 25-5-20 analysis fertilizer at the rate of about ½ pound per gallon of water in the fertilizer concentrate when fertilizer is being applied every two to four weeks, or at about 1 ounce per gallon of water in the fertilizer concentrate when fertilizer is being applied every time the plants are watered.

Injectors are used when fertilizer is being applied with each irrigation. There are various types of injectors, but the most reliable ones are water motors—the flow of water through them operates a water motor that injects the fertilizer concentrate into the water stream in exact proportion to the amount of water that is flowing through it. For an injector with a proportion of 1 to 100, 25-5-20 is used at the rate of about ½ pound per gallon of water in the fertilizer concentrate.

Application of fertilizer in the liquid form is used more commonly than dry applications because the fertilizer can be distributed on the soil more uniformly, and it requires less labor. This is particularly true with pot plants. The method to be used for making liquid applications will depend on which method is most suitable for the situation. The pump method is an accurate way to make periodic applications of fertilizer. It requires a large tank, pump, and pipe from the tank to all parts of the range.

The siphon method is a very simple system that requires very little equipment or expenditure. Siphons do reduce the flow of water. This may be no problem with pot plants, but it may be very objectionable with bench crops. The proportion with a siphon varies with water flow and difference in water pressure on either side of the nozzle. This may lead to some inaccuracies.

A good injector is a precise piece of equipment that will give very accurate proportioning when it is in good operating condition. There can be a definite advantage in supplying fertilizer with each irrigation. This can assure a uniform supply of fertilizer for the plants at all times without periods of excess and deficiency. An injector does require an initial expenditure of funds, and it must be checked periodically to be sure that it is functioning properly. This method may, however, do the best job of supplying the fertilizer needs of the plant, and it saves some labor.

- GREENHOUSE IRRIGATION SHOULD BE HEAVY BUT WELL SPACED

In the greenhouse it is possible to provide water in the amount and at the time it is needed for best growth. There should be no

Fig. 4—7. The ¾-inch Measuremix fertilizer injector is used for operations with a single hose with faucet open or with two or three hoses with faucets partially open. This size unit is used as a portable injector, and it is mounted on a cart together with the concentrate container.

Fig. 4—8. The 2-inch Measuremix fertilizer injector is a stationary installation in the water line, and it can be used for two or more hoses or for irrigation systems requiring delivery up to 100 gallons per minute.

reason for periods of drought—or flood. The importance of the use of water in growing plants is acknowledged by greenhouse operators with statements such as, "It's the man with the hose that grows the plants." He knows how to water and when to water—and maybe even more important, he knows when not to water. Irrigation not only regulates the amount of water in the soil, but it regulates the amount of air. Good root growth requires a good supply of air in the soil, and this exists when heavy irrigations are spaced far enough apart so that the soil dries somewhat between irrigations. Continual light irrigations keep the soil constantly wet and this limits the air supply. Root growth is not active in such a situation, and in spite of the abundant supply of water in the soil, the water cannot be taken into the plant because of the poor roots. The grower who uses a coarse, porous soil and makes certain that bench or pot drains perfectly simplifies his irrigation problems. Coarse soils will need to be watered more often, but they will have a good air supply even when wet.

Irrigation methods must change with the situation. Soils dry much more slowly in the winter than they do in the summer. New plantings in the winter should be spot-watered—leaving dry areas between the rows—while thorough watering of the entire bench is best on new plantings during the summer. In cold, dark weather, if there is any question about whether a soil should be watered or not, it is best to delay watering another day.

During the heating season the soil may dry differently than during the non-heating season, depending on the arrangement of the heating pipes. Pipes on the sides of the bench may cause drying of the soil right at the edge of the bench and require watering of the bench edge only. Weather conditions change radically in the fall and in the spring, and watering practices must change just as quickly to avoid serious problems.

Large plants use more water from the soil than small plants, and benches containing large plants should have to be watered more often than those containing small plants. With pot plants it is difficult to over-water small plants in small pots, but small plants in large pots must be watered very carefully.

Soils must be watered thoroughly and the water must drain freely through the bottom of the bench or pot. Thorough watering of cut flower crops requires ½ gallon of water per square foot of soil. A bench 4 feet by 100 feet would require 200 gallons of water each irrigation. With pot plants there must be enough freeboard from the top of the soil to the edge of the pot so that this area can be filled with enough water to wet thoroughly all the soil in the pot. Plants in 6-inch pots require ½ pint of water each irrigation.

If there is a build-up of fertilizer in the soil, this requires very heavy watering (leaching) to wash the excess fertilizer out of the soil. This requires several gallons of water per square foot which should be applied in the shortest period of time to prevent water-logged conditions.

Applying water by hose in hand requires a lot of time. For bench watering pressures of 60 pounds to 100 pounds are used if possible as water can be applied faster and labor is saved. A water breaker should be used on the end of the hose as this breaks the force of the water and prevents compaction of soil. The water faucets are usually located in every other walk about every 50 feet the length of the bench. A right handed grower drags the hose with the left hand and directs the end of the hose with the right hand. The end of the hose should be kept as close as possible to the soil, and for benches 4 feet wide or wider it is best to apply the water from both sides, applying the water between the rows of plants. For bench watering the grower moves down the walk extending the hose in and out of each row of plants. If the water pressure is good, he can walk right along.

For watering pot plants by hose in hand, the faucet is only partially opened to produce a gentle flow of water. Pots must be watered one at a time, and the only way that this can be done properly is to direct the end of the hose to each pot and keep it there until the pot area above the soil is filled with water. If the water is too forceful, soil is washed out of the pot; it is not possible to fill the pot evenly with water; and a generally poor job of pot watering is done. The smaller the pot the slower the flow of water must be. It takes some time and practice to learn how to water plants properly. Pots must be level on the bench or the water will spill out the low side, and the pot will not be watered evenly.

Various irrigation systems are used for watering bench crops. If they are properly installed and used, they can do a good job of irrigation and the labor formerly used for this purpose can be devoted to other essential jobs. Liquid applications of fertilizer also can be made through most irrigation systems. Regardless of the irrigation system used, it is not capable of performing the job without supervi-

Fig. 4—9. Irrigation systems on cut flower benches do a good job of supplying water to the soil and plants, and they save considerable labor time. This particular system consists of a plastic pipe at each side of the bench with 180° plastic nozzles spaced every 30 inches.

sion. Some qualified individual needs to determine when and how long to irrigate. The system cannot make that decision. Any irrigation system needs to be inspected regularly to make sure that it is operating correctly. If it is a nozzle system, some nozzles may clog and leave dry areas. If the system is connected to a water source, the valve may develop a leak and keep a portion of the bench water-logged. Irrigation systems can be excellent for most greenhouses. These comments are not to detract from their worthiness, but only to call attention to the necessity for supervision.

A common irrigation system for bench crops consists of ¾ inch plastic pipe around the perimeter of the bench with plastic nozzles spaced evenly on it, positioned to deliver the spray of water toward the center of the bench. For crops such as roses and chrysanthemums that do not have heavy foliage near the soil only 180° nozzles are used

Fig. 4—10. This irrigation system uses black plastic tubing with small diameter holes spaced about 4 inches apart on the top side the length of the tubing. The tubing inflates as the water is introduced into it, and fine streams of water spurt out of the holes. This is a "trickle" or "piddle" irrigation system.

on benches up to 4 feet in width. The nozzles are spaced about 30 inches apart. One water inlet can be used up to 100-foot benches and then one additional water inlet should be furnished for each additional 50 feet of bench. For crops with heavy bottom growth, or on benches wider than 4 feet, 45° nozzles are alternated with 180° nozzles about 20 inches apart. Water inlets should be provided every 50 feet of bench.

Black polyethylene pipe is used commonly as it is easy to work and inexpensive. Plastic insert fittings are used on polyethylene pipe. To install the nozzles, a hole is made in the pipe at the proper place with a sharp pick and the self-tapping nozzle is screwed in. Polyethylene pipe expands in warm temperatures and contracts in cold temperatures. The pipe should be installed during warm weather, stretched, and anchored at each end. Polyethylene pipe installed in cold weather "snakes" badly in warmer weather because of the expansion in length.

Vinyl (PVC) pipe can be used without anchoring and with a minimum of support as it is semi-rigid and handled in much the same way as steel pipe. It comes in 20-foot lengths, fittings are cemented, holes are drilled, and threads tapped. PVC pipe costs more per foot, but generally it makes a much more satisfactory installation than polyethylene pipe.

There is a bit of a problem in the sterilization of the irrigation system. Theoretically, it can be steam sterilized at the same time the soil is being sterilized. However, it must be handled very carefully since plastic pipe becomes very soft at high temperatures, and any weight on it would cause it to become deformed. In addition polyethylene pipe probably would decompose on direct contact with steam pipes. Usually the irrigation system is raised during steaming, and any disinfecting is done with chemicals such as Morsodren or a combination of Dexon 35 and Terraclor 75.

Irrigation systems for pot plants are not as numerous. A system that has been used successfully employs small diameter, black polyethylene tubes from the water line on the bench to each pot. An irrigation system for pot plants can save a tremendous amount of labor, but some good man must supervise the system to make sure that it is doing the job as well as hand watering or better.

There are several modifications of the pot plant irrigation system. The one that probably is the most adaptable uses a ½ inch or ¾ inch black, polyethylene pipe the length of the bench as a water main, and the small diameter (.045 ID) black, polyethylene tubing is inserted directly in holes punched in the water main. All of the small diameter tubes must be the same length, and they extend from the water main to the pot to be watered. Since this tube is light, it either must have a

Fig. 4—11. For applying water to a cut flower crop with hose in hand a water breaker should be used on the hose to reduce the force of the water or the fingers should be held below the stream of water to cause it to fan-out as illustrated here.

Fig. 4—12. The three hose attachments at the left produce sprays of water and they are used for watering seedlings or small plants. Use the faucet only partially open so that the spray is gentle enough for the young plants. The three hose attachments on the right are water breakers. They are used to reduce the force of the water without much reduction in water volume. They are used with faucet open fully for watering cut flower crops.

Fig. 4—13. The Fogg-it nozzle is an attachment for the hose that produces a very fine spray or fog. It can be used very satisfactorily for watering seed flats and young seedlings.

Fig. 4—14. To water pot plants with hose in hand the faucet must be only partially open and the end of the hose is placed at the lip of each pot until freeboard space is filled with water.

Fig. 4—15. The Chapin system for watering pot plants provides a small diameter plastic tube for watering each pot simultaneously. There are several variations of this method of pot plant watering. This illustrates the use of a single water main per bench with a small diameter leader tube to each pot. This system does an excellent job of watering pot plants and much labor time is saved. (Chapin Watermatics photograph)

Fig. 4—16. A weight is used on the end of each small diameter plastic tube. It is placed in the pot easily and does not dislodge. (Chapin Watermatics photograph)

Fig. 4—17. This is a permanent installation on the bench for watering pot mums. It is made of rigid plastic, and the downspouts are placed at the proper spacing for the pot mums. When the plants are set on the bench each one is placed under a spout, and it remains there until the crop is finished.

weight on the end or be pinned to the pot in order to keep it in the pot.

The system can be turned on and off by hand, but Chapin has devised some methods based on weight of the water applied so that once the system is started in operation, it shuts off automatically when a given amount of water is applied.

CHAPTER 5

Reproduction of Plants

CHAPTER 5

The most common means of plant reproduction in the greenhouse are by seed and by cuttings. Grafting, budding, and layering are more specialized types of plant reproduction that are used only with certain kinds of plants.

- **PROPAGATION BY SEED IS SEXUAL PROPAGATION**

The seed is the result of the pollen being transferred from the male portion of a flower (stamen) to the female part (pistil), and the seed inherits some traits from both male and female parents. Most of the flowers that are used in greenhouses have both male and female parts and in natural conditions are self-pollinated. Since the seed can acquire some traits from each parent, it is possible to develop new and better varieties by bringing together the right parents in cross-pollination and getting some good features from both.

Practically all of the snapdragon and petunia seed that is used is F-1 hybrid. Of course F-1 hybrids are used because they have some better features than plants grown from seed that is produced by self-pollination. When a pure-line plant is self-pollinated the seed produces plants that are identical to the parent. To produce F-1 hybrids the seedsman uses two pure-line parents, placing the pollen from one parent on the pistil of the other parent. When cross-pollination is done in the same way between pure-line parents, the resulting F-1 seed always produces the same hybrid plant. Thus by keeping the pure-line parents and making cross pollinations when desired, the seedsman can produce the F-1 hybrid seed as it is needed.

Seeds contain a tiny plant (embryo), a food supply, and seed coats. Seeds vary greatly in size and the larger the seed, the greater the supply of food in the seed. Tiny seeds have a very small food supply, and for that reason they must be planted close to the surface

Fig. 5—1. Emasculating a petunia is one of the steps in the production of F-1 hybrid seed. (Bodger Seeds, Ltd., photograph)

of the soil so that the plant from the newly germinated seed will reach the light rapidly and be able to manufacture its own food by photosynthesis.

- **IN PROPAGATION OF PLANTS FROM SEED, TWO SEPARATE PHASES NEED TO BE CONSIDERED**

First the seed must germinate, and when this occurs the seed coats break and the embryo plant starts its growth. For germination to take place the seeds must be kept in a uniformly moist and warm place which may be in the dark. The length of time required for germination varies with conditions and kinds of seeds, but the seeds commonly used in the greenhouse require a week or less.

The second phase is the growing of the young seedling until it is large enough to be transplanted (pricked-off). The young seedling will be grown at cooler temperatures than those required for germination of the seed. It must be placed in the best possible light; continuous air movement should be provided; and constant surface misting is replaced with only periodic, thorough watering. Seed flats must be watched carefully so that they are shifted from "germination surroundings" to "seedling surroundings" as soon as the seed is germinated.

● GERMINATION OF SEED

Seed can be sown in many kinds of containers, but quite often wooden flats that are about 3 inches deep are used. Soil or mixtures of soil and other materials can be used to sow seed in. It should be made up of small particles and finely screened as there must be good contact between the seed and the soil in order to keep the seed uniformly moist. The smaller the seed, the finer the soil should be. The seed flat should be filled almost to the top with the soil as that will allow for good air movement around the seedling later. The soil must be firmed and leveled. Soil and flat must be carefully steam sterilized as disease

Fig. 5—2. Pollination of petunias is one of the steps in the production of F-1 hybrid seed. (Bodger Seeds, Ltd., photograph)

organisms thrive in the same warm air and moist surroundings that are provided for the seed.

Sow the seed in rows as this provides for better air circulation around the seedlings, and they are also easier to prick-off. It is better to sow the seed too sparsely rather than too thickly. Tiny seed such as snapdragon or petunia should be sown right on the surface or covered very lightly. Larger seed can be sown more deeply.

For germination the seed must be kept uniformly moist. This can be done by moistening the flat after sowing and then putting a waterproof cover over it so the surface does not dry, or the flats can be left uncovered and placed under a misting system.

The initial watering of the seed flat must be done carefully. The soil does need to be completely and uniformly wetted, but the water must be applied in such a way that the seed is not disturbed. It is possible to sub-irrigate the seed flats by placing them in a pan containing about 2 inches of water. In a few minutes the water soaks up through the soil, and when the soil surface is uniformly wet the seed flat is removed from the pan. If the seed flat is watered with hose in hand, a nozzle must be used on the hose that will provide a fine mist or fog so that the water can be applied without disturbing soil or seeds. Be sure that the entire soil mass is entirely wet.

If the seed flat is thoroughly watered and then covered, no more water may need to be applied until after the seed is germinated. The cover for a seed flat must adequately seal the top of the flat so the moisture stays in the flat. A pane of glass is commonly used for covering the flat as this serves the purpose well and most greenhouses have glass on hand. If glass is used, however, and the seed flats are located in the sunlight, paper or some other opaque material should be placed over the flat also, or the temperatures under the glass will become much too high in the sun. Plastic film can be used successfully to cover seed flats. In some instances polyethylene bags are used to enclose the entire flat.

After covering, the seed flats must be inspected daily or more often to determine if the soil surface is uniformly moist, if there is any evidence of the start of disease, and if there are signs of germination of the seed. If there is some drying of the soil surface, the soil should be misted lightly. If there is some evidence of disease, which may be indicated by mold or cobweb-like growth on the surface of the soil, the cover must be raised lightly to provide some air circulation over the soil surface. Such a seed flat must then be watched even more carefully as enough air circulation must be given to stop the growth of the disease organisms but not so much that the soil surface becomes so dry that the seed dries and fails to germinate. The first indication of seed germination is a faint white speck by each seed, and this changes

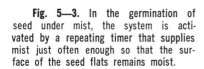

Fig. 5—3. In the germination of seed under mist, the system is activated by a repeating timer that supplies mist just often enough so that the surface of the seed flats remains moist.

to green rather rapidly if the flat is in some light. This evidence of germination is easier to detect if the seeds are sown in rows. At the first signs of germination the cover should be raised, gradually giving the seed flat more air circulation. The maximum amount of air circulation should be allowed but the soil surface must not be allowed to dry. Seed flats at this stage must be watched carefully. As more air is given, the soil surface will need to be misted periodically to prevent drying of the newly germinated seed. The cover is removed completely as soon as this can be done without causing undue drying of the surface.

If the seed is germinated under a misting system, the misting period is about 5 seconds. The seed flats should be misted often enough to keep the surface moist at all times. Mist may need to be provided as often as 5 seconds every minute or as seldom as 5 seconds every 5 minutes. Mist may need to be applied during the night as well as during the day. In the heating season the night air in the greenhouse may be very dry. If there is any evidence of drying of the surface, the frequency of misting should be increased. If there are signs of the growth of disease organisms, the frequency of misting should be decreased as much as possible and air circulation increased. As soon as germination is noticed, the frequency of misting should be reduced until only occasional mistings are given during the day as needed.

Keep the seed flats in 70° temperature constantly until the seed is germinated, and then gradually reduce the temperature to the regular growing temperature for that particular crop. Temperature is quite critical for germination. If a 70° temperature greenhouse is not available, thermostatically controlled soil heating cables could be used under seed flats.

Air movement is not a problem until the seed is germinated. After that proper ventilation is needed for the good growth of the seedling and to reduce the possibilities of disease. Several disease organisms grow rapidly in warm, moist, and stagnant surroundings, but they can be controlled if air movement is provided.

A few types of seeds require some light before they will germinate. Most of the kinds that are used in the greenhouse germinate in either light or dark; however, as soon as the seed is germinated, light is needed for good growth of the seedling. Right after germination they may need to be partially shaded from the sun, but the light should be increased as rapidly as possible.

● **GROWING THE SEEDLING**

Many of the conditions that are necessary for the germination of seed are not suitable for the young seedling. The change from "germination surroundings" to "seedling surroundings" needs to take place as rapidly as possible and yet not so fast that the young plant is affected adversely.

Unfortunately, seed flats can fit into spare corners, and it is easy to overlook the fact that the best sunlight is needed for good growth of the seedling. Be sure that the flats are not in the shade of gutters, buildings, or tall plants.

The seedling should be grown at the same temperature as the crop will be during forcing. Although the seed is germinated at 70°, petunia and other bedding plant seedlings are grown at 50°, and snapdragon seedlings are grown at either 50° or 60° night temperatures, with daytime temperatures 5° to 10° higher.

The soil should not be allowed to become dry, but as the seedlings grow the waterings should be spaced farther apart. Water the soil heavily each time, but do the watering early enough in the day so that the soil surface and the plants dry rapidly. Use a nozzle that gives a fine mist or fog for watering seedlings. A good watering can be given with such nozzles and still not disturb the plants or the soil.

Give the seedlings good ventilation; air circulation fans will be helpful also. Most seedlings are susceptible to damping-off diseases, and good air circulation keeps the soil surface and the plants drier and less likely to become invaded by the diseases. If there is any evidence of disease, drench the soil and the seedlings with Morsodren or a combination of Dexon 35 and Terraclor 75.

Prick-off the seedlings from the seed flat as soon as they can be handled. This will be when the leaves are just big enough to permit the seedling to be handled by the leaves. When they are transplanted at this stage the growth will be most rapid and of best quality. Usually seedlings are not in seed flats long enough to require any fertilizer, but if there was no fertilizer in the soil at all at the time of sowing, a liquid application a week or two after germination could help.

- **PROPAGATION BY CUTTING IS ONE OF THE MEANS OF VEGETATIVE PROPAGATION OF PLANTS**

Vegetative propagation of plants is possible because stems and some other vegetative parts of plants are able to form roots and shoots

Fig. 5—4. An unrooted carnation cutting.

Fig. 5—5. Carnation cuttings being stuck in the propagation bench. Holes are dibbled in the perlite and peat mixture, and after the cuttings are stuck they are watered heavily. Note the mist lines above the propagation bench.

when placed in the right conditions. This is a good method of increasing the number of plants of the same kind, and it is a common means of propagation in the greenhouse. Stem tip cuttings are used, but in some instances the stem is cut into sections each of which has only one or two leaves. These are called leaf-bud or eye cuttings. Leaf-bud cuttings are rooted in much the same fashion as stem-tip cuttings, and after rooting the shoot develops.

It is important to have a reliable source of cuttings for propagation as the right plant must be reproduced and the new plants must be disease-free also. It is best to have the plants that are used for cuttings in a separate area so they can be given the special attention that is needed. These plants are called stock plants or mother blocks. Stem-tip cuttings are taken from the stock plants and rooted in the propagation bench.

The methods for making cuttings vary with the kind of plant, but regardless of the plant, the leaves should not be trimmed as that would reduce the food supply for the cutting. Dusting with hormone powder such as Rootone or Hormodin produces more roots on most cuttings in a shorter time. However, many cuttings root satisfactorily without using any hormone at all. It is better to dust or spray the hormone on the cuttings rather than to dip them as disease can be transferred from one cutting to the next by dipping. It is possible to use too much hormone on the cuttings and cause a burn that can be the start of a disease infestation.

Moisture, temperature, air, and light must be regulated very carefully in the propagation area. The cutting has been severed from its source of water, and it does not have roots to absorb water. It is best to put the cutting in high humidity so that loss of water from it is at a minimum. Some very fine automatic misting systems are available for propagation benches. These can be set so that they operate just often enough to keep the leaves moist. These systems are relatively inexpensive, and they make it possible to do a much better job of rooting cuttings. If such a system is not used, the cuttings must be misted by hand as often as possible, and the area needs to be shaded to reduce the amount of water loss from the cuttings. During the non-heating period of the year it should be necessary to operate the mist system only during the day. However, during the heating season

Fig. 5—6. An unrooted geranium stem tip cutting.

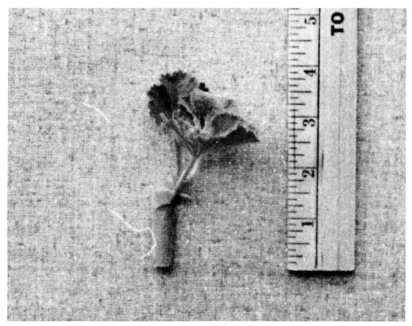

Fig. 5—7. An unrooted geranium leaf bud cutting.

Fig. 5—8. Geranium stem tip cuttings in the propagation bench. Geranium cuttings are watered heavily after sticking, and then they are watered sparingly after that.

Fig. 5—9. An unrooted rose, 2-eye cutting.

Fig. 5—10. An unrooted hydrangea stem tip cutting.

Fig. 5—11. Unrooted hydrangea leaf bud cuttings.

the mist should be provided both day and night as the greenhouse air is dry at all times then.

The rooting material in which the cuttings are stuck must be fine enough so that it is in close contact with the cutting and keeps the cutting moist, but it should not be so fine that it does not drain readily and thus become water-logged. Many different rooting materials have been used, and many can still be used successfully. Perlite or mixtures of perlite and peat moss are used very commonly. The propagation bench must be steamed carefully each time before use, and any handling equipment that is used in the propagation area must be sterilized also. Before sticking the cuttings the bench is thoroughly watered. The bench is then lined or dibbled for the proper distance for the cuttings to be stuck. Cuttings are stuck in the propagation bench as closely as possible without the leaves overlapping. Large-leafed cuttings such as poinsettia are placed 2 inches apart in the row with 5 inches between rows while smaller cuttings such as geranium or carnation are spaced much closer. Lines in the propagation bench are made by drawing a large knife along a straight board that is placed across the width of the bench. If holes are dibbled for each cutting, this is done with a dibble board that makes severals rows of holes across the bench. After the cuttings are stuck in the bench the propagating material is firmed on each side of the cutting by placing a board the length of the row on each side and tapping it with a weight. The cuttings are then watered thoroughly. When cuttings are first stuck they need to be misted for about 5 seconds each minute, and as roots form the frequency of misting is reduced until little or no mist is given the last day or two before they are lifted from the propagation bench.

Accurate temperature control is essential in the propagation house. The air temperature should be maintained at the usual growing temperature for that crop during forcing and the bench temperature should be 10° higher. The best method for heating benches is with thermostatically controlled soil heating cables. Cuttings root very slowly in cool temperatures, and roots may be damaged at temperatures that are too high. Thermostatically controlled electric heat for the propagation bench can speed the rooting of cuttings.

Fig. 5—12. Rooted azalea cuttings. (Blackwell Nurseries photograph)

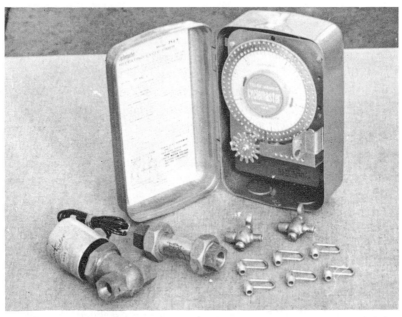

Fig. 5—13. Other than the pipe on which it is installed the equipment needed for a propagation mist system is electric water valve, water strainer, mist nozzles, water cocks, and a repeating timer. (Jednak Floral Co. photograph)

Fig. 5—14. A chrysanthemum propagation bench with mist line installed but not operating.

Fig. 5—15. The same chrysanthemum propagation bench with mist line operating. The misting is regulated by a timer that can be adjusted to provide mist just often enough to keep the leaves moist.

The propagation bench must be well aerated. Water must drain from the bench freely, and the rooting material in the bench also must drain well so that there is a good supply of air in the bench for the cuttings. Rooting is more rapid in a well-drained, well-aerated propagation bench. The quality of the roots is better, too. Roots in a well-aerated propagation bench are heavy and branched while roots in a poorly drained bench are long and thin.

One of the advantages of rooting cuttings under mist is that they do not have to be shaded. The periodic misting prevents water loss from the cutting even in the sun, and therefore when the cutting starts to root the top growth that it makes while it is in the propagation bench will be of good quality because of the sunlight. Cuttings rooted in shaded propagation benches can be soft and stretched, depending on how the shade is handled. If the propagation area does not have a misting system, the cuttings will have to be well shaded from the sun to prevent undue water loss from the cuttings. It is best to shade the glass with shading compound as well as to have a removable cloth that can be placed above the propagation bench. In some instances it may be necessary to cover the cuttings in the bench directly, but this is poor practice as it establishes moist, stagnant conditions that are conducive to the start of a disease infestation. Use the minimum amount of shade possible over the propagation bench. When it can be done, remove shade as the cuttings root so that the cuttings will be exposed to stronger light toward the end of the rooting period.

Usually there is no fertilizer of any kind in the propagation bench. When the cuttings are first stuck there is no need for any; however, when rooting starts, most cuttings will benefit from a liquid application of a complete fertilizer. This is particularly true of cuttings propagated under mist.

It is best to lift the rooted cuttings from the propagation bench as soon as they are rooted. The cuttings are lifted from the bench by inserting a broad knife below the roots with the right hand, and with the left hand on top of the cuttings, the rooted cuttings are lifted from the bench and placed in a flat. It is necessary to give the roots some support from below, or they can be torn from the cutting easily. There is no advantage in leaving the cutting in the bench until a large root system is formed. It is better to plant the rooted cutting early and have the development of the root system take place in the pot or in the bench where the plant is going to be grown. There is some difference in the speed of rooting of cuttings. If you wait until all of the cuttings in the batch are rooted, some will be rooted too much. It is best to lift the cuttings when the majority of them are rooted, and those that are not rooted can be restuck, planted, or discarded.

The moist and warm conditions that are provided in a propagation house are ideal for the growth of disease organisms if any are present. The benches and all handling equipment must be carefully sterilized before each use. It is equally important that the propagation stock be free from disease. The identification of disease-free stock is something of a problem as some of the disease organisms can be present in the inner tissues of the plant, but with no disease symptoms visible outwardly as yet. In many instances the spores of the disease organisms are present on the exterior of the plant, but they are not noticeable. It is necessary to maintain continual inspection of the stock along with various laboratory methods to be sure that stock is disease-free.

Stock that has been processed through a laboratory is known as culture-indexed stock. Depending on the process that is used, the stock may be cultured for just one or for possibly several disease organisms. An entirely different technique is needed to indicate the presence of virus than is needed to detect the fungus that produces Verticillium wilt, and methods to detect the presence of bacteria may differ from those that can indicate whether or not a fungus is in the plant tissue. The production of culture-indexed stock can be handled only by the specialist propagator as it requires a well equipped laboratory and highly trained personnel. The chrysanthemum industry could not exist without the fine system of culture-indexing that was developed by the specialist propagator. Great advances have been made, too, in eliminating the incidence of carnation and geranium diseases through culture-indexing.

- **GRAFTING AND BUDDING ARE MEANS OF PROPAGATION THAT ARE USED FOR SOME PLANTS**

The most common means of plant propagation in the greenhouse is either by cuttings or seed; however, some plants propagate better by grafting or budding. Roses are propagated by budding and some azaleas by grafting.

The principle is roughly the same in both grafting and budding. A greenhouse variety plant is started in growth on the roots of another plant by joining a small portion of the plant with the root or the stem base just above the roots. In grafting, a stem (scion) is joined with the roots, and in budding, only a bud of the greenhouse plant is transferred to the base of the other plant.

The growth in diameter of plant stems takes place immediately under the bark. If the under-bark portion of one plant is joined with the under-bark portion of another, the two portions may grow together or unite. In grafting, the stem just above the roots is cut in such a way that the scion can be placed on it to match the under-bark portions of both parts. Many different types of grafts are made, but a common one in the greenhouse is to cut root stock stem and scion on a similar slant, then match one edge of each and tie them together. It is not necessary to use root stock and scion of the same diameter and match both sides.

In budding, a patch of bark containing the bud of the greenhouse plant is placed in a slit made in the bark toward the base of the root stock plant and tied. In some instances, new varieties of roses are "top-budded" in other rose plants in the greenhouse in order to increase the new variety rapidly. As the name indicates, the bark patches containing the new variety bud are placed on the upper portions of the rose plant. After the bud patch unites with the plant the stem is cut just above the bud, and growth starts in the new bud, producing a flowering shoot eventually.

Greenhouse roses are budded on manetti root stock; the budding is done in the field in southwestern United States. The manetti cuttings are planted in the field during the winter and the budding is done during the late spring and summer.

Grafting is usually a greenhouse operation. After the graft is made the plants are placed in a closed case in which humidity and temperature are maintained at a high level until the scion knits with the root stock.

CHAPTER 6

Cut Flower Crops

CHAPTER 6

There is a steady demand for cut flowers the year around. For this reason the producer tries to plan his crops so that he has uniform production at all times.

As the name indicates, these crops are flowers that are cut from the plant. The act of harvesting the flowers—or cutting—may require about 25% or more of the total time spent working with the crop. In spite of moving right along and constantly deciding if the flower is ready for cutting and where the cut should be made, this is an ideal time to view the whole area and do some thinking and planning. This may be the only chance all day to get over the entire area bench by bench, and it is the best time to make note of what work needs to be done.

• CUT FLOWER BENCHES USUALLY ARE LOW AND NARROW

Benches for cut flowers must be fairly narrow so that the plants at the middle of the bench can be reached conveniently for pinching, disbudding, tying, and cutting. Most cut flower benches are either 3½ feet or 4 feet wide. Ground benches are more satisfactory for cut flowers as they provide the most head room for the plants. This is important particularly with roses and carnations on a two year rotation. Regardless of the material of which it is constructed, the bench must drain perfectly.

• ROOT GROWTH AND TOP GROWTH ARE BEST IN COARSE SOILS

Soils for cut flowers are used for several years, and it is very important that a good soil mixture be used as it is difficult to make adjustments after the crop is planted. Use a coarse soil. With most soil it is best to add organic matter such as strawy manure, straw, poultry litter peat moss, or peanut hulls. In some instances it will help to add an aggregate such as haydite, or gravel. The aggregate, however, needs to be coarse—no smaller than ¼ inch. Each time before benching crops, a fresh supply of organic matter should be added. A coarse soil will drain readily, and will have a good air supply in the soil even when it is wet. Root growth can be excellent in such a soil.

The bench should not be completely filled with soil as this would not allow enough water to be put on the bench to soak through the soil. The surface of the soil needs to be at least 1 inch below the top of the side board on the bench, and the soil must be level or the water

Fig. 6—1. Benches for cut flowers need to be raised from the ground enough to isolate the soil from disease organisms and insects, but they should not be so high that it is difficult to work with the crop. Using the width of a concrete block for the leg with 2 inch x 4 inch wooden cross supports, the bench is about a foot above the ground. Note the good spacing of the bottom boards of the bench to provide perfect drainage of water through the bench.

Fig. 6—2. Spot-watering the plants leaving dry areas between the rows allows the soil to dry more rapidly and this aids root growth of young plants. This is a particular advantage during the winter.

Fig. 6—3. As soon as possible after cutting, flowers are placed in water in vases. They are then graded, bunched, and placed in a refrigerator until they are shipped. These cut flowers are attractively wrapped with transparent film. It provides protection for the flowers in shipping, but does not obscure the flowers.

will run to the low spots and the plants will be watered unevenly—and grow unevenly.

• CUT FLOWERS MUST BE WATERED THOROUGHLY

Enough water must be applied to the cut flower bench so that the water drains freely through the bottom of the bench. This will be applying water at the rate of ½ gallon per square foot of soil. The soil then should be allowed to dry somewhat before it is watered thoroughly again. It is necessary to dig into several locations of the bench to determine if irrigation is needed. Just looking at the surface of the soil is not enough as the top dries more rapidly than the lower levels where the roots are. If the watering is done with hose in hand, a breaker should be used to reduce the force of the water. Applying the water directly to the soil from a hose compacts the soil, and this reduces the amount of air in the soil and limits root growth.

If an irrigation system is being used, make sure that all of the water outlets are functioning each time and that the coverage of the entire bench is good. Be certain that enough water is applied to drain freely through the bottom of the bench. With some irrigation systems it is best to "double water." The system is turned on for just a few minutes to water the surface soil, and then a complete watering follows an hour or so later. This can give better distribution of water throughout the entire soil, particularly if the soil was a little dry before watering.

• PLANTS NEED A CONSTANT SUPPLY OF FERTILIZER

Several types of fertilizer and various methods of fertilizer application can be used successfully. If either phosphorus or calcium is needed, they should be incorporated in the soil before planting.

If the soil has been used for several years and phosphorus added before each crop, the phosphorus supply might be high enough. Usually calcium should be added before each planting. If the pH is below 6.5, either agricultural limestone or hydrated lime should be added at the rate of 5 pounds per 100 square feet. If the pH is between 6.5 and 7.0 but the calcium is below 200 ppm, gypsum (calcium sulfate, land plaster) should be added at 5 pounds per 100

Fig. 6—4. Bunched carnations being packed for shipment to the wholesale flower market. They must be packed carefully to prevent breakage, and they must be protected from freezing temperatures during the winter and excessive heat during the summer.

square feet. If the phosphorus is less than 5 ppm, superphosphate should be added at the rate of 5 pounds per 100 square feet.

Actually the decision on what kind of fertilizer to add to the soil before planting should be based on soil tests that have been made on that particular bench for the past few months. The supply of phosphorus or calcium in the soil and the acidity of the soil do not change rapidly. By reviewing the past soil tests it is possible to see if there is a gradual shift taking place, and it is better to make the decision on that trend rather than on one test made just before planting.

Fertilizers containing nitrogen and potassium are supplied regularly after the plants are in the bench. The fertilizer supply is very critical in the first month of growth of the plants. Too much fertilizer in the soil can limit root growth, and not enough fertilizer shortly after planting can cause permanent stunting of the plant. It is best to know what the fertilizer supply is in the soil before planting by having soil tests made, and then check the plants daily for root growth. Good root growth should be under way within a week after planting, and the fertilizer program then is started.

If the equipment is available for applying fertilizer in the liquid form, it is best to use an analysis of approximately 25-0-25 or 25-5-20. The phosphorous and calcium have been added before planting, and nitrogen and potassium are the fertilizers that will be needed regularly during the growth of the crop. The nitrogen supply is the most critical, and it is leached from the soil most easily. The nitrate level should be maintained at a minimum of 50 ppm. If fertilizer is being applied with each watering by means of an injector, 25-0-25 or 25-5-20 fertilizer should be used at the rate of ½ pound per 100 gallons of water applied until soil tests show that a different amount is needed. If the fertilizer is applied from a tank at intervals of every two to four weeks, either of these fertilizers should be used at the rate of 3 pounds per 100 gallons of water.

Fertilizer can be added to cut flower crops in the dry form, but it is more difficult to make a uniform application and care must be taken to keep the fertilizer off the plants. If the fertilizer lodges on leaves or stems, it causes burns and actually may kill some of the plants or parts of plants. Dry fertilizer of 10-5-5 analysis should be applied at the rate of 1½ pounds per 100 square feet, every two to four weeks. The rate of application is based on the amount of nitrogen. If a 5-10-5 fertilizer were used, it would be at the rate of 3 pounds per 100 square feet. The soil must be moist when dry fertilizer applications are made, and then the fertilizer is watered-in afterward.

The fertilizer supply in the soil not only depends on the amount of fertilizer applied, but it also depends on how porous the soil is, how heavily and how often the soil is watered, and the size of the plants that are growing in the bench. It really is not possible to use an arbitrary rule to fertilize every two weeks and have uniformly good results. If testing cannot be done regularly and a fertilizer injector is not used, make the first fertilizer application on the first watering after root growth has started, and then make a repeat application with each seventh watering. It is much safer, however, to test the soil at least once a month and base the fertilizer application on the test results. If

Fig. 6—5. Daffodil bulb production fields in Oregon. (From Kodachrome by C. F. Doucette)

a complete fertilizer test cannot be made, a Solubridge test will tell you rapidly whether fertilizer should be added or not.

Bulbs

• DAFFODIL (NARCISSUS)

The bulbs are produced on the West Coast, and after digging in the fall they are precooled by the producer. The bulbs are graded by size and by whether they are "single nose" or "double nose." The "single nose" bulb consists of one bulb and produces only one flower. The "double nose" bulb is actually the mother bulb plus one or more daughter bulbs that are still attached, and it produces two or more flowers. For greenhouse forcing the double nose #1 daffodil bulbs are used primarily because the flowers are larger, and more flowers are obtained per bulb.

There are several different kinds of daffodils, but it is the large, trumpet types that are forced in the greenhouse. The variety grown in the greatest quantity is King Alfred. Daffodils often are forced early in the season only, because later flowers from the Southern and Western outdoor bulb fields are shipped in.

Daffodil bulbs are received at the greenhouse early in October. They are planted bulb to bulb in boxes, placed outdoors, watered, and covered with about 6 inches of soil and 8 inches of straw. This maintains an even ground temperature, and it prevents freezing later in the fall. While buried outdoors the bulb should develop good root growth during early fall, and the shoot should start to develop. The cooler temperatures later in the fall cause the bulb to mature so that it will force into flower earlier when it is brought into the greenhouse.

The outdoors bulb storage should be located conveniently to the greenhouse and in a well drained place. Keep in mind that it will be necessary to dig the boxes of bulbs in all kinds of weather, and that they must be accessible. The boxes will need to have labels on sticks that will be visible above snow drifts, and the kinds of bulbs should be placed in the area so that the boxes can be dug up in rotation.

In some instances the bulbs are placed in either common or refrigerated storages after they are planted. These are operated at 50° until root and shoot development are good, then the temperature may be dropped to 35°. The boxes will need to be watered periodically in the storages. There is expense involved in operating a storage, but the bulbs can be handled more quickly and conveniently.

• FORCING DAFFODILS IN THE GREENHOUSE

Whether the bulbs have been stored outdoors or in storages, they cannot be forced satisfactorily in the greenhouse until the roots are well developed and the flower bud is out of the neck of the bulb. This can be determined by carefully feeling the leaves just above the neck of the bulb. The daffodil bud will not be at this stage until about the first week of December.

At 55° to 60° in the greenhouse the flowers can be cut in three to four weeks after the first bulbs are brought in. Some boxes of bulbs are brought into the greenhouse at regular intervals to provide a succession of flowering. The later in the season they are brought in,

Fig. 6—6. Iris bulb production in Washington. (From Kodachrome by C. F. Doucette)

the quicker they force.

The daffodils do need to be kept well watered after they are brought into the greenhouse, but no fertilizer is used for forcing bulbs.

Daffodils are cut just above the neck of the bulb, and leaves as well as flower are cut. They may be cut in full flower or in tight bud depending on how they are going to be used. If they are going to be shipped for any distance they are cut in tight bud as they ship best that way, and they open satisfactorily to full flower when placed in warm temperatures. After cutting, daffodils are bunched in dozens and placed in water in the refrigerator.

• IRIS

The primary source of iris bulbs is the West Coast although they also are grown in Holland and Japan. The bulb producer cures and precools or retards the bulbs before shipping them to the greenhouse grower. Iris bulbs are graded by circumference in centimeters, and they range from 8 centimeters to 12 centimeters. The larger bulbs force a little faster, and they produce larger flowers. Several iris varieties are available, but Wedgewood iris is the only one that is used in quantity. It is possible to have iris in flower from the middle of December until May by planting the bulbs from the first week in October until the last week in February.

● CONTINUOUS CROPPING OF IRIS

It is best to plant iris bulbs directly in the bench in which they are going to be grown. The bulb producers ship iris weekly from October through February, and the growers, by making successive plantings, can flower iris from December through May. Special pre-cooled iris are shipped the first two weeks in October. Then precooled bulbs are shipped until the last week in November. These are followed by retarded iris bulbs. The larger size bulbs should be used for the first planting as they force more successfully early than the smaller bulbs, but deep soil must be used so it can be kept constantly moist.

Planting is simple since all that needs to be done is to push the bulb into the soil with just the tip extending above the soil. The bulbs are planted about 2 inches by 4 inches, and watered in well. Iris soils must be kept uniformly moist at all times, and if the temperature is warm in the fall it is helpful to put a light mulch of straw over the soil. Iris are usually grown in 60° houses; however, they can be grown cooler in which case it will take a little longer for them to flower.

● FORCING REGULAR IRIS

Regular Wedgewood iris are planted the first week in November in the northern states and November 15 in the South. At 55° to 60° night temperatures the 10-11 cm. bulbs flower the last week in January, 9-10 cm. bulbs the first week in February and 8½-9 cm. bulbs the third week in February. Other varieties of regular iris are planted from November 15 to December 1, and they flower early in April.

Iris planted outdoors in November and then mulched heavily after the first freeze will flower in May. Usually only the smaller size bulbs are used for outdoor culture.

Fig. 6—7. Tulip bulb production fields in Washington. (From Kodachrome by C. F. Doucette)

Fig. 6—8. Bulbs flower faster and more uniformly if they are placed in cool temperatures for a few weeks before being forced. Here bulbs are covered with soil and wood chips outdoors in the fall, and they will be brought into the greenhouse from December and on for forcing.

● **IRIS NEED A CONSTANT SUPPLY OF WATER AND GOOD LIGHT**

If iris are planted in boxes, be sure that the boxes are at least 4 inches deep to hold enough soil to maintain uniform moisture. It is best to let the boxes remain in one location rather than move them. Very often roots are broken in moving, and this limits the water intake. Insufficient water for iris causes blasting of the flower bud or blindness. Blindness also occurs when roots are damaged by an over-supply of fertilizer in the soil. Iris do not need to be fertilized, and if the bulbs are planted in soil previously used in the greenhouse, some of these soils may contain too much fertilizer.

Iris should be grown in the best light possible. Poor light conditions may contribute to blindness.

If the iris make a lot of leaf growth but they do not flower or flower on very short stems, the trouble is related usually to improper temperature treatment of the bulb before planting.

Iris flowers are cut in fairly tight bud as they handle well that way in the refrigerator, and they open very well when brought out into warmer temperatures. The stem is cut just above the neck of the bulb.

Carnation

Carnations are started from rooted stem tip cuttings that are planted in the spring. The cuttings are pinched and some of the shoots that develop are pinched, too. By late summer, when pinching is discontinued, the average plant has at least 10 shoots. Flower production starts in the fall and continues throughout the year until the plants are removed. It usually is desired to leave the plants in production through May as the demand for flowers is good in the spring. This is a one year rotation of carnations following carnations. It allows for good plant growth during the spring and summer and heavy production during the winter and following spring, but it does not provide for flower production during the summer. In order to have summer flower production as well as through the rest of the year, two year crops are used or else carnations are rotated with another crop.

For two year crops, half of the area is replanted each year. Thus half of the area will be in production during the summer and the entire area the rest of the year.

When carnations are rotated with another crop they are planted in the spring, and then followed fifteen to eighteen months later with either snapdragons or mums planted in the fall. The area is returned then to carnations the next spring. If about one half of the entire

Fig. 6—9. Carnation cuttings being stuck in a propagation bench. Note the mist line over the propagation bench. (Yoder Bros., Inc., photograph)

carnation area is rotated in this way and the rest on the one year rotation, this provides for some flower production during the summer and good production during the rest of the year.

● STEM TIP CUTTINGS ARE USED FOR PROPAGATION

Carnation cuttings are 4 inches to 6 inches long, and they should not be trimmed. They are stuck to a depth of 1 inch in the propagation

bed and spaced about 1 inch in the row and about 4 inches between
rows. The medium is then firmed around the rows, and the bench is
watered thoroughly.

The rooted cuttings should be lifted from the propagation bench
when the roots are about ½ inch long. Further rooting will not be
helpful. Carnation roots are not tough, and they will need to have
support from below while lifting or the roots will be torn from the
cutting. This is more of a problem in sand than in perlite. At 50° air
temperature and 60° to 65° temperature in the bench, rooting requires
about three weeks. Carnations root well in several different materials.
Some of the better ones are perlite, coarse sand, and perlite and peat
moss. The cuttings must be of good quality, heavy, and entirely free
from disease. To get uniformly good cuttings it is necessary to devote
an area just to the production of cuttings, and if this cannot be done, it
is better to purchase good quality cuttings from a reliable source.

Either unrooted or rooted carnation cuttings can be stored at 33°
for several weeks satisfactorily. They must be kept moist, but they
should not be completely sealed. A simple method is to place moist
sphagnum in the bottom of cellophane bags, place 25 cuttings per bag,
fold or staple the top and set the bags upright in a box in the refrigerator.

- **PLANT THE ROOTED CUTTING IN THE BEST
  POSSIBLE GROWING CONDITIONS**

Keep it growing actively. This is done best by planting the rooted
cutting directly in the bench in which the plant will be grown. The
young plant will get good light spaced out in the bench, and the water
and fertilizer requirements are provided better. If the rooted cuttings
are potted first, this should be for no longer than three weeks.

Soil and all handling equipment must be carefully steamed for
carnations, as they are very susceptible to several diseases. Set the
plants as shallow as possible. Root growth will be more rapid and the
plants less susceptible to Rhizoctonia stem rot. You should be able to
observe—by a little careful digging around the base of the plants—
new root growth three or four days after planting, and within a week
after planting very little wilting during the heat of the day. This is
good evidence that the soil is well drained, that fertility is not too

high, and that your watering methods have been good. Regular applications of fertilizer then can be started.

The fertilizer program for carnations can be about the same as for the other cut flowers except more attention must be paid to the supply of boron. Boron deficiencies have occurred in several soils, and the effects on carnations are varied. Some of the symptoms of boron deficiency are few petals per flower, death of young flower buds, ring around the calyx, and splitting of the leaf base with a shoot growing through it. To be sure that the soil has a sufficient supply of boron, carnation soils should be given an application of 1 ounce of borax per 100 square feet once a year. This is a very small amount of material and it must be applied as a liquid to get even distribution. It is possible to get boron toxicity if applications are made more often.

Carnations are spaced about 7 inches by 8 inches, or in some instances, two rows are planted side by side with 14 inches to 16 inches between the double sets of rows. As they grow, the plants must be supported so that they grow upright. This can be done by stretching wire the length of the bench between each plant and then lacing string across the bench by each row of plants. The first set of wires is placed about 4 inches above the soil, and the distance between succeeding sets is increased gradually. This provides a square, upright column for the support of each plant. However, all of the stems will not remain in their own squares, and periodically the wayward stems will need to be "poked" into their squares to assure straight stems. There is a lot of weight on these supports as the plants grow. A good system of cross bars is needed to hold the wires firmly in place.

● **THE PLANTS SHOULD BE PINCHED AT THE RIGHT STAGE OF GROWTH**

For the first few weeks after planting, the leaves that develop on the plant will be closely spaced. About four to six weeks after planting, the stem starts to elongate, and the leaves are spaced farther apart. The plants should be pinched at the first internode that shows this elongation. This will leave six sets of leaves or more on the plant, and very often side shoots already will be developed below the pinch. The pinch is made by breaking the stem to the side. The plant then may be allowed to flower, or pinching can be continued depending on the kind of cropping that is desired.

Fig. 6—10. Carnation stems at various stages of growth, and the proper place to pinch the stem or cut the flower. Left to right: a young shoot that is not far enough advanced for pinching; this stem has started to elongate and the pinch should be at the first internode that shows elongation — this type of pinching should be done on young plants until about August 1; after August 1 the pinch is made in the same position on the stem but only on stems that are farther advanced and forming a flower bud; the stem is cut in the same position, and at the time of cutting there should be one or two well-formed side shoots below this position — the cut is made above at least one of these side shoots.

Fig. 6—11. Showing the position of pinch or cut on carnation stems. Left to right: the early season pinch; the pinch from August 1 to mid-September; cutting the flower. If the pinch is made as shown after August 1, some flower production will be eliminated in September, October, and November. However, flower production will be increased during the important marketing period from January through March. If these stems had not been pinched, the return flower crop from stems cut in September through November is in May and June. Additional flower production is not needed at that time as flowering is normally very heavy anyway because of favorable weather conditions.

The carnation plant can produce flowers any time of the year, but flowering is much more rapid in bright, warm weather than in dull, cool weather. A stem pinched in late spring will produce a flower in about three months. However, it requires about eight months for a flower from a stem pinched in the fall. If pinching is discontinued on the young plants in July, flower production then starts in the fall with a return crop in the late spring. Since the market is better in winter than it is in the fall, the young plants should be pinched to provide good production of flowers during the winter. Continue pinching until about the middle of September; however, after the first of August, pinch only the stems that have started to form flower buds. By doing this, the early fall flowers are eliminated and replaced with greater winter production. The place to pinch is still the same—at the first internode that shows elongation. Pinching the stems that are ready once a week is all right, but in the last of August and early September daily pinching of the stems that are ready is best because the weather conditions that follow are such that the difference of a day or two in pinching at that time of the year can make a difference of several weeks in time of flowering.

- **TEMPERATURES IN THE CARNATION HOUSE SHOULD BE 50° AT NIGHT, 55° ON CLOUDY DAYS, AND 60° ON BRIGHT DAYS**

Too warm temperatures may produce weaker stems and smaller flowers. Too cool temperatures may delay growth. Too much tempera-

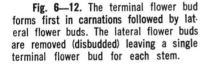

Fig. 6—12. The terminal flower bud forms first in carnations followed by lateral flower buds. The lateral flower buds are removed (disbudded) leaving a single terminal flower bud for each stem.

ture differential between night and day or widely fluctuating temperatures will increase flower malformation and splitting. In many areas summer temperatures are too warm for carnations. Pad and fan cooling can reduce house temperatures 10° or more, and this can improve plant growth considerably and improve the quality of the flowers.

● DISBUD CARNATIONS EARLY

Some carnation varieties are known as spray types or miniatures. All or most of the flower buds that develop on these stems are allowed to flower. If any disbudding is done on these types, it is only the removal of the top or terminal bud. With the standard or large flowered varieties, only the top or terminal bud is allowed to flower and the side buds are removed or disbudded. This is done as soon as

Fig. 6—13. A carnation stem after disbudding.

they can be handled. If they are left on too long, the flower size decreases. At the proper stage, they can be broken out to the side without damage to the top bud. Be sure that the leaves are not torn or removed during disbudding as that can cause crooked stems. The three to four buds below the top bud do need to be removed, but don't continue to disbud down too far on the stem or some of the leafy shoots will be removed that would produce the next flower crop.

• CARNATIONS ARE CUT WHEN THEY ARE FULLY OPEN

As compared with some other flowers, carnation flowers develop rather slowly, and it is necessary to cut flowers only three times a week except in very warm weather when they might be cut daily. To determine whether or not the flowers are fully open, the flower must be viewed from the top. If there are several closely packed petals at the center of the flower, it is left for the next cutting. Since the flowers are commonly above eye level, it is necessary to bend the stem so that the top of the flower can be seen in order to decide if the flower is ready for cutting. The flowers are then cut with a knife in one hand and are carried with the other.

The decision on where to cut the stem is based on getting the longest possible stem without harmful effect to the plant and the subsequent crop. During the fall the stem must be cut so that a rapid return crop will follow. The stem should be cut at the first internode that shows elongation. That very often will be just above two or three leafy shoots that are well developed on the stem. This type of cutting may be continued on plants that are going to remain in production longer than one year; but for plants that are going to be removed in May or June, long stems may be cut after the first of the year, as there would not be enough time for a return crop anyway.

The flowers are cut in the morning, graded, bunched, and placed in vases in the refrigerator. The next morning they are packed and shipped or brought to the market. Methods of bunching vary with the area of the country, but the object is to put 25 flowers of the same quality of a variety per bunch. Culls, splits, or shorts are either discarded or bunched together and sold as work or utility flowers.

• RED SPIDER MITE AND APHIDS ARE THE MOST COMMON PESTS

At one time, two spotted mite or red spider could not be controlled on carnations during warm weather, and that was the primary reason that carnations were not carried over for a second year's production. Adequate controls now are available, and with some attention to duty this pest can be controlled. This is a tiny pest and very often you can see the results of his work before you actually see the red spider. The leaves turn a dull, gray-green color, and they look stiff and straight. Very often the spiders first start to work about midway down on the plant and toward the tip of the leaf. They may be on the under side of the leaf, but on carnations it is not uncommon to find them on the upper surface of the leaf also.

Aphids are the other most likely pest to inhabit a carnation house. They are large enough to be seen quite easily. They usually work on the stem tips.

Thrips can be a problem, particularly in early summer. They cause streaks on the flowers. The thrips themselves may be difficult to see unless you knock them out of the flower onto a paper, or search the inner part of the flower by spreading the petals. Thrips can float in through the ventilators and continuously reinfest the plants, so the area must be treated continuously during thrip season. With these pests or others, immediate action is the answer for good control!

• START WITH DISEASE-FREE CUTTINGS AND
KEEP THEM IN CLEAN CONDITION

Several diseases are common with carnations. Fusarium wilt, bacterial wilt, and Rhizoctonia stem rot all can produce symptoms that are quite similar. There is some wilting of the plant followed by a change in color to dull gray-green, and then finally to straw color. There usually is evidence of stem damage at or near the soil line. Fusarium and bacterial wilts are more common on older plants, and Rhizoctonia occurs more readily on younger plants. If symptoms of these are noticed, have the disease identified by an expert since the methods of treatment vary depending on which disease is present.

Fusarium stem rot usually starts in a stem or two in the plant and then progresses downward until the whole plant may be involved.

Very often this disease gets its start in the stem after a flower is cut. Periodic spraying with captan can control this disease.

Rust does not start on carnation leaves unless there is moisture on the leaves. The best preventive for rust is to make sure that the leaves are dry. If rust is present, spray frequently with zineb.

There are several virus diseases of carnations. The most common symptoms are mottled or streaked leaves. If the presence of virus diseases is suspected, do not use this stock for propagation.

- **CARNATIONS SPORT OR MUTATE READILY, GIVING RISE TO NEW VARIETIES**

There is a constant need for larger flowers, longer stems, more fragrance, better colors, more production, faster growth, stronger stems, and a number of other desirable traits. The variety, William Sim, alone has given rise to hundreds of excellent varieties. There will be many new and valuable varieties found in the future by patient and careful observers.

Preference for flower color varies with the market. Commonly, however, the demand for red carnations is greater for Christmas and Mother's Day than it is during the rest of the year. Light pink carnations and white carnations are grown in the greatest numbers as the year around demand is best for them. A small percent of medium pink, yellow, crimson, and variegated carnations are also grown. The Sim varieties are excellent in all color classes except crimson and purple.

There are several varieties of spray or miniature carnations available, but the best all around varieties have been Elegance and White Elegance.

- **CARNATIONS GROW BEST IN AREAS THAT HAVE GOOD LIGHT DURING THE WINTER AND COOL TEMPERATURES DURING THE SUMMER**

Carnations are grown widely throughout the country with the exception of the extreme South where the summer temperatures are too warm. Most retail growers produce some carnations as it is a crop that can be grown quite well in small quantities, it works in well with other "cool" crops, and it is a convenience to have some flowers at the greenhouse that can be cut for immediate use. Wholesale carnation growers are scattered throughout the northern states, but the greatest carnation production is in the New England states, the Denver area of Colorado, and the San Francisco area of California. Carnation growers have located in these areas either because the winter light conditions are better or the summer temperatures are cooler or both conditions are more favorable.

● SPLITTING IS COMMON WITH CARNATIONS

In a split carnation the calyx is split and some of the petals extend through the split making an unsightly, lopsided flower. There is a great deal of difference in the splitting characteristics of carnation varieties. Whenever possible, varieties should be grown that are known to have a low percentage of splitting. Many different causes have been named for splitting, but other than the heredity factor it seems that great temperature changes may be the most important cause. There should not be more than about a 10° temperature difference between day and night temperatures for carnations. Splitting is most common during fall and spring when daytime temperatures may be high and night temperatures may be lower than usual because the boiler is not being used during the mild weather in order to economize.

When carnation petals cup upward, it is referred to as sleepiness. To the customer this is an indication of old flowers, but actually sleepiness can occur in fresh flowers, too. It happens in some varieties much more readily than in others, and of course those varieties should be avoided. Sleepiness in carnations can be produced by some gases, such as illuminating gas or gas as given off from ripening fruit or vegetables. There have been many instances in which carnations have been ruined simply by keeping them in the same refrigerator with apples or other fruit.

Carnation stems are often weaker than desired during the dark days of the winter, as stem strength is related to the amount of sunlight that is available to the plant. Unfortunately the Sim varieties do not have as heavy stems as some of the other varieties, but their other characteristics are so good that they are grown widely in spite of this problem.

Fig. 6—14. The flower on the left is a well-developed carnation. The one on the right is called a split. Some varieties split more than others, and careful regulation of temperatures will reduce the amount of splitting.

Fig. 6—15. The flower on the left is a well developed carnation. The one on the right is called sleepy—the petals cup upward.

Chrysanthemum

Chrysanthemums are grown from rooted stem tip cuttings. Depending on how they are handled, the entire crop flowers from three to five months after planting; the flowers are cut in about a week's time; the plants are removed; and the bench is prepared for replanting. In order to have continuous flower production throughout the year it is necessary to have continuous plantings. Many chrysanthemum programs are designed to provide an equal area in flower each week of the year.

- **STEM TIP CUTTINGS ARE USED FOR THE PROPAGATION OF CHRYSANTHEMUMS**

Depending on the variety, they root in two to three weeks with air temperature of 60° and bench temperature of 70°. The difficult part in chrysanthemum propagation is not in rooting the cuttings but in having good quality cuttings of the right varieties at the time when they are needed. For this reason rooted chrysanthemum cuttings usually are bought from specialist propagators.

- **PLANT THE CUTTINGS IN GOOD SOIL**

Chrysanthemums may be grown as single stem plants spaced about 4 inches by 6 inches, or pinched plants spaced about 6 inches by 8 inches. For flowering during the winter this spacing may be increased. They are planted directly in the bench in which they are going to be grown. Planting as shallow as possible is recommended as this promotes rapid root growth, and it reduces the possibility of Rhizoctonia stem rot. Root growth and top growth, both, are much more rapid in coarse, porous soil. With chrysanthemums there should be no excuse for not having the soil in the very best condition as the same soil is replanted two to three times a year, and there is an opportunity each time to prepare the soil in the best way. This is quite a different situation than carnations, which may be planted just once a year or once every two years, or roses, which may be planted only once every four years. Mum soils should be adjusted before each crop so that they are in the best possible condition. Usually some coarse organic matter such as strawy manure, straw, or poultry litter peat moss should be added to the mum soil before each planting. If the same soil has been used for a number of years, regular additions of superphosphate may no longer be needed, but calcium should be incorporated at least once a year in the form of agricultural limestone, gypsum, or hydrated lime. Mum soils need to be steam sterilized before each planting. This keeps diseases under control, eliminates weeds, and makes the soil more porous.

Most mechanical tillers pulverize the soil too finely, and because of the way they are used, the bottom layer of soil is not disturbed. In many instances this causes a hard layer of soil at the bottom of the bench that prevents the good drainage of water through the soil. Hand spading of the soil takes a bit longer, but it is the best way to assure that the soil is mixed well but still coarse and porous.

• CHANGE WATERING-IN METHODS WITH WEATHER CONDITIONS

Since mum cuttings are planted any time of the year, procedures need to be varied according to the weather conditions at the time. During the summer the cuttings are watered-in well and then misted periodically for several days after planting. This reduces wilting and allows the cutting to start in growth more rapidly.

When planted during the winter the cuttings should be spot-watered—definitely leaving dry areas between the plants. This allows the soil to dry more rapidly, and root growth is faster. Leaving heating lines on around newly planted benches in the winter will also be an aid. New root growth should be evident within a week after planting. To discover this requires some careful digging around a few of the plants. If root growth is slow, delay watering as long as possible as it is most likely that the soil is drying too slowly. Other causes of slow root growth are too much fertilizer in the soil or too cool temperatures.

As soon as good root growth starts the regular irrigation and fertilization program should begin. Make a fertilizer application with the first watering after planting. It is very important at this stage of growth that the young plant has a steady supply of nitrogen—not huge amounts at a time but a constant supply. Particularly during the winter when soils dry more slowly, it may be necessary to have some gradually available nitrogen in the soil at planting time to satisfy the needs of the young plant until the first watering and fertilizer application can be made. The growth of the young plant during the long day period should be active and lush, and this will be evident by the large leaves and heavy stems. This is promoted by thorough applications of water and an ample supply of fertilizer.

When the short day period is started the amounts of water and fertilizer that are applied should be reduced until the flower buds are developed. Thorough watering and regular fertilizer applications then are resumed.

• WELDED WIRE FABRIC IS GOOD SUPPORT FOR MUMS

Chrysanthemums do not require nearly as much support as do carnations. If the same varieties are grown in the bench or if all the varieties reach about the same height, it is possible to use a single layer of wire to support them. If the varieties are of different heights, two layers are sufficient. Welded wire fabric with 6-inch by 8-inch spacing of wires gives excellent support and it is convenient to handle. After the soil is prepared for planting the wire fabric is placed on the soil, and one or two cuttings are planted per square depending on whether a pinched or single stem crop is going to be grown. As the young plants grow, the wire fabric is raised to give support to the upper part of the plants.

• THE LENGTH OF DAY DETERMINES WHETHER THE MUM
PRODUCES LEAFY GROWTH OR FLOWERS

When chrysanthemums are growing in long days they produce leaves as they grow in length, but they will not flower as long as they are kept in long days. As soon as they are placed in short days they start to form flower buds, and then they will produce flowers if they remain in short days. Chrysanthemums are photoperiodic—flowering is dependent on the length of day. In natural conditions they flower only in the fall because the days get short enough in August for them to form flower buds, and as the days remain short the plants flower in October to January depending on the variety.

Until the effect of day length on mums was understood, they were flowered only during the natural period in the fall. It then was learned that flowering could be prevented or delayed by making artificially long days with electric lights, and that flowering could be promoted by making artificially short days by drawing black cloth over the plants. This led to the production of chrysanthemums the year around by providing long days or short days as desired.

When chrysanthemums are planted they are given long days as this promotes leafy growth and increase in stem length. During the period from late May to the first of August the days are long naturally, and it is not necessary to extend the length of day with electric lights. During the rest of the year it is necessary to light mums for a while after planting. If they grow in long days until the stems are about 12 inches long and then are placed in short days, they will produce flowers on about 36-inch stems. That is about the right length for most markets.

• LONG DAYS CAN BE PROVIDED BY ELECTRIC LIGHTS

Several different lighting systems are used to provide long days. A minimum of 10 foot candles can be supplied by using 60 watt lamps 4

Fig. 6—16. To provide long days artificially 60-watt lamps can be used spaced 4 feet apart and 2 feet above the plants. Aluminum plates can be used as reflectors.

Fig. 6—17. Fluorescent light can be used to provide artificially long days. The 4-foot, 40-watt units are spaced 4 feet apart.

feet apart and 2 feet above the plants. With such a system it is necessary to raise the lights as the plants grow to maintain complete coverage of the plants at the edge of the bench. It is most efficient and economical to provide the light at the middle of the dark period—about midnight. In order to reduce the power demand, half the area can be lighted before midnight and half afterwards. Other than the cost involved there is no problem in lighting too long each day. Some growers light the plants an hour each night even during naturally long days and 4 hours a night from the first of August to the last of May. For minimum lighting no additional light is used during the summer; 2 hours each night in August; 3 hours each night in September and October; 4 hours each night in November through February; 3 hours each night in March and April; and 2 hours each night in May. Someone needs to check each day to be sure that the lights are being turned on and off the correct benches and that each lamp is operating. Failure of lights to operate for one night may be of little consequence, but failure for several nights can produce malformed flowers.

● SHORT DAYS ARE PROVIDED BY PULLING
  BLACK CLOTH OVER THE PLANTS

A twelve-hour day is short enough, and this must be provided artificially by black cloth from the middle of March to the first of September. Quite commonly the plants are covered with black cloth each day before the workers leave, and it is removed in the morning when they come on duty. This is a method of getting the work completed during the regular work hours, but it does place the plants in shorter days than necessary. It deprives the plants of some sunlight, and during the heat of the summer, temperatures under the cloth are too hot and remain hot longer. This situation is further aggravated in areas where they have Daylight Savings Time as the plants are covered an hour earlier in the afternoon. If it is not possible to have the cloth pulled by the night men, it is best to have a crew come in at

Fig. 6—18. Short days are provided artificially for plants by drawing black cloth over them.

Fig. 6—19. Day-night time switch for control of lights and the photoperiod for chrysanthemums. (Jednak Floral Co. photograph)

about 7:00 P.M. just to cover the plants. The cloth then can be removed when the regular crew comes on in the morning.

It may be necessary to use black cloth during naturally short days when adjacent benches are being lighted. In such a situation it is best to use drop cloths between the benches rather than covering the bench. Covering the bench during the winter can deprive the plants of some much needed sunlight.

- **CROWN BUD FORMS WHEN CONDITIONS ARE NOT JUST RIGHT**
  FOR CONTINUED DEVELOPMENT OF THE FLOWER BUD

For the formation and the proper development of flower buds of chrysanthemums the plant must be in short days and in a suitable temperature. With anything less, either a flower bud is not formed or a partially developed flower bud known as a crown bud is formed. If the day length is not quite short enough, or if it fluctuates from time to time, or if the temperature is too high during short days, crown buds form. Usually the stem below the bud appears stretched, and the bud does have a rather crown-like appearance. The shoots below the crown bud are leafy, vegetative shoots. When this occurs with spray mums the sprays of flowers are then on long stems, and the spray is loose and awkward to handle. With standards or disbuds that form crown buds the decision must be made either to keep the crown bud and disbud all of the side shoots or to remove the crown bud and leave the shoot just below the bud to continue in growth. If the stem is approximately tall enough and the conditions (day length and temperature) are now suitable for development of the flower bud, it

Fig. 6—20. The terminal flower bud forms first in chrysanthemums followed by lateral flower buds. With standard and disbud type flowers the lateral flower buds are removed (disbudded) at this stage leaving a single terminal flower per stem. With spray chrysanthemums the lateral flower buds are not disbudded resulting in a spray of flowers per stem.

Fig. 6—21. The plant on the left is a spray chrysanthemum. The lateral or side shoots are not removed, and each stem forms a spray of flowers.

The plant on the right is a standard chrysanthemum. All the lateral or side shoots have been removed (disbudded), and there will be a lone, large flower per stem.

then is best to retain the crown bud. If the stem is not going to be long enough, the crown bud should be removed and the shoot just below it retained to develop the new flower bud. If this is done while the crown bud is small, there will be no noticeable crook in the stem. Short days and proper temperature conditions then must be provided to assure the formation of a good terminal flower bud on the new stem.

With some varieties, too cool temperatures may prevent flower buds from forming, or crown buds may be formed. In some instances rosette type growth occurs in cool temperatures, and this type of growth may continue until the temperature is increased. Crown buds that form in cool temperatures also have leafy shoots below them, but the stem is not stretched.

Chrysanthemums will form flower buds (crown buds) even in long days if the stem has grown long enough, but if the long days are maintained the crown bud does not continue to develop into a flower. Propagators have learned that stem tip cuttings that are made from long shoots on the stock plants form crown buds early, whereas stem tip cuttings made from short shoots on the stock plants do not. Growers have learned that planting too early results in formation of crown buds. Mums that are grown on carefully timed schedules do not form crown buds from too lengthy a growing period in long days.

- MUM VARIETIES DIFFER IN LENGTH OF TIME REQUIRED
  FOR FLOWERING AFTER START OF SHORT DAYS

Because of this definite response to day length, it is possible to predict quite accurately the flowering date of chrysanthemums after

Fig. 6—22. A disbudded chrysanthemum stem.

the start of short days. Some varieties require a shorter period than others after the start of short days. The so-called garden varieties of the northern states flower seven or eight weeks after the start of short days. Thus in natural conditions with short days starting in mid-August, the 7- and 8-week response varieties flower in October before the killing frosts in the northern states so that it is possible to use these varieties outdoors. Farther south it is possible to use 9-, 10-, or 11-week varieties for the outdoor garden as they flower in natural conditions in November before the killing frosts for those areas. Some varieties flower as slowly as fifteen weeks after the start of short days. It is the 9- through 15-week varieties that are used in the greenhouse, and it is primarily the 9-, 10-, and 11-week varieties that are used in the year around programs.

Propagators and sellers of chrysanthemum cuttings list the different varieties by their response group, and publish schedules that are used for flowering mums throughout the year. The schedules list dates for planting, pinching, lighting, shading, and flowering. The schedules provide for starting the plants in long days, pinching after some new growth is made by the young plant, continuing long days until the stems are about 12 inches long, and then giving short days until the plants flower. Because plants grow more slowly during the winter, the schedules provide for a greater number of long days during the winter than the summer. By using these schedules it is possible to make plans for weekly flowering of chrysanthemums. To do this requires about twenty benches for pinched crops and about eighteen benches for single-stem plants.

For more favorable climates, such as the mid-Southern states, reduce the schedule by one week of long days.

This schedule is for 10-week varieties. The total length of time for flowering any response variety would be the same. The slower response varieties would be furnished correspondingly fewer weeks of long days after the pinch. The faster response varieties would be given correspondingly more weeks of long days after the pinch. For instance, an 11-week variety planted October 1 would be furnished seven weeks of long days after the pinch, and a 9-week variety would be given nine weeks of long days after the pinch.

SUGGESTED SCHEDULE FOR GROWING CHRYSANTHEMUMS
IN THE NORTHERN HALF OF THE UNITED STATES

Planting Date	Weeks of Long Days		Weeks of Short Days	Total Weeks from Planting to Flowering
	Before Pinch	After Pinch		
May 1-June 10	2	3	10	15
June 10-July 15	2	4	10	16
July 15-Aug. 5	2	5	10	17
Aug. 5-Aug. 20	2	6	10	18
Aug. 20-Aug. 25	3	6	10	19
Aug. 25-Sept. 15	3	7	10	20
Sept. 15-Oct. 30	3	8	10	21
Oct. 30-Nov. 15	3	7	10	20
Nov. 15-Dec. 30	4	6	10	20
Dec. 30-Jan. 15	4	5	10	19
Jan. 15-Feb. 10	3	5	10	18
Feb. 10-Mar. 1	3	4	10	17
Mar. 1-May 1	3	3	10	16

For single stem crops the length of time from planting to pinching is saved, and the total time for producing the crop is reduced by that amount.

Schedules are based on average growing conditions. If the actual conditions are not as suitable as the average, the mum flowers will not attain the usual size. The experienced mum grower uses the schedule for reference, but he varies it to adjust for conditions that actually exist at the moment. For instance, there may be more sunlight and warmer temperatures than usual this particular fall and the growth will be faster and heavier than normal. Under these conditions, a week or possibly more could be taken from the scheduled time and still have good sized mums. If, however, the weather turns unusually cool and dark, the plant growth may be so slow that some extra time should be added to the schedule.

- SCHEDULED GROWING TIME IS LONGER DURING THE WINTER AND SHORTER IN THE SUMMER

Since plant growth is slower during the cool, dark weather of winter, the time scheduled for growing the winter crop is longer. The scheduled time is varied with the season so that approximately the same quality flowers are produced at any time of the year. For pinched crops it takes as short a time as fifteen weeks for plants started in May, and as long a time as twenty-one weeks for plants started in mid-September and October. For single stem crops, the length of time from planting to pinching is saved, thus the total time required is from thirteen weeks to eighteen weeks depending on the time of the year.

It can be seen from the schedule that the number of weeks of short days remains constant for a variety for any time of the year, but the number of weeks of long days varies with the expected weather during the year. The slowest growth of the newly planted cutting is expected in the period from November 15 through January 15, and four weeks of growth are allowed before the pinch during this period. Only half this time is required during the warm, bright period of the year from May 1 through August.

- **MUM ROTATION SCHEDULE ASSURES THAT SPACE IS FULL AND FLOWERS ARE ON HAND WHEN NEEDED**

It takes some planning ahead to make a chrysanthemum rotation that will fit the best needs. If benches are simply planted whenever they are empty, surely time, effort, and valuable space are going to be wasted.

From a mum rotation it is desired to have as even production throughout the year as possible, and of course the benches should not be idle any more than necessary. Rotations can be adjusted to fit the situation at hand. There is always more than one solution, but the best rotation provides the quality flowers at the time they are needed and the available area is kept as active as possible.

The crop usually is cut-off by the scheduled flowering date; however, some time is needed for reworking the soil and sterilizing, so a week is allowed between the scheduled flowering time and replanting. Two sample rotations are given. Using a 10-unit area with pinched crops, this rotation provides for a crop about every two weeks, and each unit has about 2¾ crops per year. The 9-unit area in single stem rotation provides for about the same interval between crops, but the crop time is shorter and about 3¼ crops are produced per bench per year. Single stem crops require about twice the number of plants as pinched crops, but since a shorter growing time is required the costs involved are about the same.

SAMPLE ROTATION FOR A 10-UNIT AREA IN PINCHED CROPS

Unit	1st Crop Plant	Flower	2nd Crop Plant	Flower	3rd Crop Plant	Flower
1	Jan. 1	May 13	May 20	Sept. 2	Sept. 9	Jan. 27
2	Jan. 15	May 20	May 27	Sept. 9	Sept. 16	Feb. 10
3	Jan. 29	June 3	June 10	Sept. 23	Sept. 30	Feb. 24
4	Feb. 12	June 10	June 17	Oct. 7	Oct. 14	Mar. 10
5	Feb. 26	June 24	July 1	Oct. 21	Oct. 28	Mar. 17
6	Mar. 11	July 1	July 8	Oct. 28	Nov. 4	Mar. 31
7	Mar. 25	July 15	July 22	Nov. 18	Nov. 25	Apr. 14
8	Apr. 8	July 29	Aug. 5	Dec. 9	Dec. 16	May 5
9	Apr. 22	Aug. 12	Aug. 19	Dec. 30	Jan. 6	May 19
10	May 6	Aug. 19	Aug. 26	Jan. 13	Jan. 20	May 26

SAMPLE ROTATION FOR A 9-UNIT AREA IN SINGLE STEM CROPS

Unit	1st Crop Plant	Flower	2nd Crop Plant	Flower	3rd Crop Plant	Flower
1	Jan. 1	Apr. 22	Apr. 29	July 29	Aug. 5	Nov. 18
2	Jan. 15	May 6	May 13	Aug. 12	Aug. 19	Dec. 9
3	Jan. 29	May 13	May 20	Aug. 19	Aug. 26	Dec. 16
4	Feb. 12	May 20	May 27	Aug. 26	Sept. 2	Dec. 30
5	Feb. 19	June 3	June 10	Sept. 9	Sept. 16	Jan. 13
6	Mar. 4	June 10	June 17	Sept. 16	Sept. 23	Jan. 20
7	Mar. 18	June 24	July 1	Oct. 7	Oct. 14	Feb. 10
8	Apr. 1	July 1	July 8	Oct. 14	Oct. 21	Feb. 24
9	Apr. 15	July 15	July 22	Oct. 28	Nov. 4	Mar. 10

• MUMS CAN BE FLOWERED IN THE FALL WITHOUT LIGHTS OR SHADE

Since this is the natural time for flowering of mums, these are commonly referred to as natural season mums. Actually many of the chrysanthemum growers have gotten so used to either lighting or shading mums that they do so even during the natural season. Of course there is some advantage in lighting or shading according to schedule as this practice does give more uniform flowering than the somewhat variable natural conditions. Lighting and shading add to expense, however, and there is an advantage in eliminating costs whenever possible.

It is possible to have continuous flowering of natural season chrysanthemums from late October to mid-December by making continuous plantings during the summer of the various response groups of mums. The 9-week varieties flower the last week in October, 10-week varieties the first week in November, and so on with the 14-week varieties flowering the middle of December. It is important to plant each group of varieties at the right time in the summer so that they finish at the right height and develop flower buds properly. The earliest flowering varieties should be planted about July 1 and followed at weekly intervals until the latest flowering group is planted about the first week in August.

Before the relationship between day length and flowering in chrysanthemums was understood, the natural season mums were planted in May and early June and they were much too tall at flowering time in the fall. Because of this early planting many varieties formed crown buds. With spray varieties this often resulted in awkward sprays, and with standard or disbud mums the decision had to be made whether or not the crown bud should be "taken." Mum growers used to pride themselves on knowing the varieties on which they could "take" a crown bud or a terminal bud. The need for this knowledge vanished with later planting of natural season mums as usually only terminal buds are formed.

Before year around chrysanthemums became common, mums were known as a 50° crop. During the heating season they were handled as a 50° crop, but since only natural season mums were grown it was at the naturally warm temperatures during the summer. Actually they were in 50° temperatures only after the flower was formed. Shortly after mums had been grown at various times of the year it was learned that they are really a 60° crop, and many of the most popular varieties do not form flowers uniformly at cooler temperatures.

Mum varieties are listed in catalogs by their response group or the date of natural flowering. By planting varieties from each of the groups it is possible to have flowers throughout the natural flowering season.

- **THE PINCH IS MADE AFTER THERE IS ENOUGH NEW GROWTH ON THE PLANT TO PERMIT THE PINCH TO BE MADE IN THIS NEW GROWTH**

Remove as little as possible of the tip of the plant in making the pinch. This is commonly referred to as a soft pinch. If the pinch is made in this way, the two or three leaves below the pinch will enlarge greatly after the pinch, and the shoots that develop will be heavy and

PLANTING SCHEDULE FOR NATURAL SEASON MUMS

Plant	Pinch	Flower	Response Group
July 1	July 15	Oct. 25-Nov. 5	9-week
July 8	July 22	Nov. 5-Nov. 15	10-week
July 15	July 29	Nov. 15-Nov. 25	11-week
July 22	Aug. 5	Nov. 25-Dec. 5	12-week
July 29	Aug. 12	Dec. 5-Dec. 15	13-week
Aug. 5	Aug. 26	Dec. 15-Dec. 25	14-week

strong. Usually several shoots develop following the pinch; however, all but the two strongest ones are removed as soon as they can be handled. In some instances three shoots may be retained on the outside row of plants.

Some mums are grown single stem, and they are not pinched. Flowers can be produced with single stem crops from two to four weeks faster than with pinched plants. It also may be possible to produce somewhat larger flowers during the winter on single stem plants.

- CHRYSANTHEMUMS SHOULD BE GROWN AT 60° NIGHT TEMPERATURE AND 65° TO 70° DURING THE DAY DEPENDING ON WHETHER IT IS CLOUDY OR SUNNY

In the last few weeks before flowering sometimes these temperatures are reduced gradually 5° to 10° in an effort to increase the size of the flowers. This is possible, but it also slows the development of the flowers. Very often it is not practical to vary the temperature because any delay in flowering will affect the scheduled replanting, or because plants of different stages of growth are in the same house. Temperature can dramatically affect flowering on some chrysanthemum varieties. Many of the varieties that commonly are grown will not flower satisfactorily at temperatures below 55°. Others will not flower if they are kept at 65° or higher.

- THERE ARE MANY SHAPES, SIZES, AND COLORS OF CHRYSANTHEMUMS

These characteristics, coupled with the excellent keeping qualities of mums, explain the wide popularity of the chrysanthemum. They are classed as standards, disbuds, or sprays. The standards are

Fig. 6—23. An incurved, standard chrysanthemum. (Yoder Bros., Inc., photograph)

Fig. 6—24. A spider, standard or disbud chrysanthemum. (Yoder Bros., Inc., photograph)

Fig. 6—25. A pompon, spray chrysanthemum. (Yoder Bros., Inc., photograph)

Fig. 6—26. A decorative, spray chrysanthemum. (Yoder Bros., Inc., photograph)

Fig. 6—27. A single, spray chrysanthemum. (Yoder Bros., Inc., photograph)

Fig. 6—28. An anemone, spray chrysanthemum (Yoder Bros., Inc., photograph)

the largest flowered mums. The side shoots on standards are removed as soon as they are large enough to be handled, thus only one flower per stem develops. Some standard varieties produce flowers as large as 5 to 6 inches in diameter. On the most popular standards the petals curve upward and inward toward the center, and these are referred to as incurve. The standards whose petals do not curve in quite so much are called semi-incurve. There are some large flowered varieties that have decorative form—the petals are straight and do not incurve.

As the name implies, disbuds also are grown with a single flower per stem—the side shoots are removed or disbudded. Many different forms are grown as disbuds. The smaller sized incurves, semi-incurves, and decoratives may be used. If the flowers are large enough, single, spider, and fujii type mums are grown as disbuds.

Spray mums are not disbudded. All of the side shoots are allowed to flower. This produces a spray of flowers per stem. In some instances the top or terminal bud may be removed if the spray appears to be tight, but other than this no disbudding is done. The pompon is probably the best known form of mum grown as a spray. It has ball shaped flowers. The smaller sized daisies, anemones, and decoratives also are grown as spray mums.

• CUTTING AND GRADING THE FLOWERS

The first flowers in a planting of chrysanthemums that are ready to cut are the largest and the best quality. The entire crop is cut in a period of a few days, and the flowers which are slower to develop are the smaller and weaker ones. The flowers should be cut when they are just about fully open. At this stage most of the petals at the center of the flower will be expanded and not tightly packed. There is no problem in knowing where to cut the stem. It is cut as long as possible since the remainder of the plant is going to be discarded anyway.

Standards are graded by size of flower, and they are sold by the dozen. Spray chrysanthemums are bunched by weight—usually 9 ounces per bunch. Disbuds are sold by the dozen, and if any grading is done, it is by size of flower or length of stem. Chrysanthemums are bunched and placed in vases in a refrigerator overnight and then taken or shipped to the market.

● CHRYSANTHEMUMS ARE PRODUCED WIDELY THROUGHOUT THE COUNTRY

Retail growers usually produce some mums. Some may flower them only in the fall during the natural flowering season, but other retailers grow chrysanthemums at various times during the year when they can fit them in with their other crops. The retail grower should have small quantities of many different varieties in order to produce a wide assortment of types, colors, and sizes for use in his retail shop. In most instances the retail grower should grow only the amount of flowers that he can use in his own shop, and with mums that would require planting small units regularly in order to have a constant supply in flower.

Chrysanthemums are grown by wholesale growers in all areas of the country, but the greenhouse operators produce many more standard mums than they do spray mums. They attempt to arrange their rotation in order to have even production at all times. In most markets the chrysanthemum is not a holiday flower, and no extra production is planned for the holidays.

Northern greenhouse operators may grow some mums outdoors during the summer. These are spray mums, as it is more difficult to protect the larger flowered types from rain, wind, and disease damage outdoors than it is the smaller flowered varieties. As the outdoor temperatures may be cool sometimes, suitable varieties must be planted. Use the varieties that form flowers at cool temperatures and that do not turn pink in cool weather. Cloth houses are used for outdoor production as a better quality mum can be grown under cloth than in the open. The partial shade of the cloth produces larger leaves, heavier and longer stems, and larger flowers. It also is easier to keep pests under control. In the northern states the earliest outdoor mums are planted the first part of May, and outdoor production ends in October or early November.

Large areas are devoted to chrysanthemum production in California and Florida. The Florida production is outdoors under plastic screen and flowers are produced from fall through spring. The Florida mum production is almost entirely sprays.

There are obvious climatic advantages in growing flowers in Florida. The winter light and temperature conditions are much more

Fig. 6—29. Acres of spray chrysanthemums are grown in Florida under plastic screen. (Floral Acres, Inc., photograph)

Fig. 6—30. Chrysanthemum stock plants being grown under plastic screen in Florida for the production of stem tip cuttings.

suitable than they are in the North, but there are hazards, too. Other than the threat of frost damage at some time or other during the winter, very often there are extended periods when the temperature is too low for uniform flower formation. Heavy rains and hurricane winds can be problems during the season, and the generally warm, humid climate is favorable for disease and pest growth.

California has large areas under plastic and glass, and standard mums and fujiis are produced in quantity there.

Transportation is an important factor when the producing area is at a considerable distance from the market areas. Both California and Florida producers use truck transports and air freight to get their product distributed around the country. The improvement in these shipping facilities has benefited the growers, but the shipping costs tend to neutralize the climatic advantage that the western and southern grower has over the northern growers.

• THE MOST PERSISTENT PESTS ON MUMS ARE APHIDS

They seem to be particularly adept at crawling under bud scales and escaping detection and pesticides. Aphids usually infest the upper parts of the stems, and it is very important to have them eradicated before flowering time as it is very difficult to control them on open flowers.

Two spotted mite (red spider) is a common pest on chrysanthemums. These mites inhabit the under side of the leaves, and they often get their start on the lower leaves. It is difficult to control them, too, on open flowers, and every effort needs to be made to have them in control before flowering time.

Thrips may invade the mum house once or twice a year. They infest the flower, and their activity causes streaks on the petals. With serious infestations the flowers may be damaged to such an extent that they fail to open. Thrips are small and they move rapidly. Sometimes the damage is noticed before any of the pests are seen. Usually to see them it is necessary to dislodge them from the flower by knocking it sharply above a paper. During thrips season continuous control is necessary as the pests have the ability to sail in through the ventilators and reinfest the mums almost as soon as they have been treated.

• CHRYSANTHEMUMS ARE SUBJECT TO MANY DISEASES

Some of these diseases have been so serious that for a time they threatened to put an end to chrysanthemum production entirely. Verticillium wilt was brought under control only after a method of maintaining wilt-free stock was perfected. This, coupled with thorough stem sterilization of soil and handling equipment, eliminates the disease. A stunt disease took severe toll of chrysanthemums until it was identified as a virus, and means for maintaining stock clean of this and other viruses were developed. Yoder Bros., Inc., Barberton, Ohio, primarily were responsible for devising the ways for keeping these diseases in check. It is quite clear that these two diseases will remain under control only as long as clean propagation stock is maintained.

Pythium root and stem rot, and Rhizoctonia stem rot are common on plants for a few weeks after planting. Some varieties are particularly susceptible to Pythium, and they are not planted unless the conditions can be controlled carefully. Steam sterilization of soil and handling equipment is very important in controlling these diseases. The cuttings should be planted as shallow as possible and the soil be allowed to dry somewhat between watering. Drenching the soil with Dexon and Terraclor mixtures, or with Morsodren after planting can help control these diseases.

Botrytis blight is a problem primarily on standard mums from spring through fall. With this disease the tips of the lower petals turn brown. Some varieties are more susceptible than others, and that is the reason the most susceptible varieties are not grown during that period of the year. Since constant air movement helps to prevent Botrytis infestations, air circulation fans have been an aid in combatting Botrytis.

• THE CAUSES OF TROUBLES ARE USUALLY RATHER ORDINARY

It really is quite seldom that unusual and inexplainable maladies affect mums. Most often the trouble is directly related to some rather common event. Review what has been done with light, shade, fertilizer, spray materials, water, and consider what changes have occurred in the weather. The cause of trouble usually is associated with these everyday events rather than with something new and different.

Slow start in growth after planting is common during the dark, cool weather in the winter. Growth will be even slower if the soil is heavy and poorly drained and water is applied too often. Root growth and top growth are slow even in good weather when such soil conditions exist. Too much fertilizer in the soil could also be a cause.

Failure to develop new shoots after the pinch is characteristic of a few varieties, and either those varieties should be grown as single stem plants or other varieties selected for pinched culture. Shoots break poorly on any varieties that have poor roots, particularly if they are pinched too hard. Some spray materials can cause lack of shoots after the pinch, especially emulsion base insecticides used during warm weather.

Small leaves on mum plants are caused by either lack of fertilizer or lack of water in the plant. This deficiency in the plant may be because the soil conditions are such that the root growth is poor, or it can be caused by failure to apply sufficient fertilizer and water to the soil. Mums grown outdoors during the summer will have smaller leaves in the full sun than under cloth or screen shade.

Anything that contributes to the poor growth of the plant also will cause small flowers. Not enough sunlight during the winter is a common cause. Spacing plants farther apart will be of some help. Proper use of fertilizer and water will help. Restrict the use of fertilizer and water somewhat during the flower forming period (short days), but use water and fertilizer liberally for the early growth during long days and again after the flower bud is formed.

Sunburn on the petals is sometimes confused with Botrytis blight, but the pattern of the damage is different enough that the two can be distinguished. Botrytis is located most often only on the tips of the outermost petals, and only a tip here and there might be affected. Sunburn most often affects the petals toward the center of the flower, and very often the burned petals form a complete ring as all of the petals at that same stage of growth were burned by the sun at the same time. Standard mums and some disbuds should be shaded by light cloth as they come into flower during the summer.

Delay in flowering is most likely to be associated with delay in starting short days or improper temperatures. It is quite common to have a high temperature delay on some crops during the summer.

Fig. 6—31. A crown bud is formed in a chrysanthemum when light or temperature conditions are not completely suitable for the formation or development of the flower buds.

Fig. 6—32. When a crown bud forms in chrysanthemum, shoots form in the leaf axils immediately below the bud. These will be leafy (vegetative) shoots as shown here if the plant is in long days and a suitable temperature.

Fig. 6—33. The shoots below a crown bud in chrysanthemum may also have crown buds as shown here if the light or temperature conditions continue to be variable.

Greenhouse cooling systems have reduced this, but sometimes the temperatures get too warm even with cooling systems. The flower buds of some varieties will not continue to develop at high temperatures, but the stem does stretch, making the crop too tall. Some varieties are much more sensitive to high temperatures, and their use should be avoided during the summer. Starting short days late and failure to shade the plants each night during short days can cause a delay in flowering. Using cool temperatures in the later stages of flower development slows the rate of development, and the flowering is delayed.

If the stems are too short in spite of good weather and using the right schedule, the most likely cause is too little nitrogen in the soil, particularly in the early stages of growth. It is very important in the first two to three weeks of growth that mums have some nitrogen available. If they do not, the plant is stunted, and it does not recover from this even if the nitrogen deficiency is corrected later.

There are several causes for uneven flowering. It is helpful to determine if there is a pattern of flowering that would suggest the cause. Very often the plants at each side of the bench flower first. This is associated primarily with the side plants getting more sunlight than the plants at the center of the bench. However, it can be caused by not raising the lights as the plants grow. The side plants grow above the lights—thus the plants at the center are lighted for the full period and the plants at the edge actually have their short days started earlier.

If the flowering is very early on short stems and it is scattered throughout the planting, this is an indication of a virus disease called stunt. The flowers may be distorted or off-color, too.

Mums will not flower as rapidly in poor light conditions as they will in good sunlight. The plants on the side of the bench next to the gutter or placed where a building casts shade on them will not flower as soon as the plants on the opposite side of the same bench. This produces a pattern of flowering that is lengthwise to the bench. If the black cloth that is used for providing short days is always gathered and left on the same place above the bench, the plants in the shade of the cloth will flower more slowly than the plants that are not shaded. This produces a pattern of delayed flowering for a strip across the bench.

Light leaks on plants that should be in short days will delay the flowering of those plants. This may be caused during naturally short days when a bench is being lighted adjacent to a bench that should have short days. The light from the lighted bench might cause delay in flowering of the plants on the side of an adjoining bench. This causes a flowering and height pattern lengthwise in the bench.

In naturally long days, if the black cloth is not closed carefully or there is a tear in the cloth, the plants in that vicinity will be delayed in flowering.

If a light fails to operate and it is not detected for a period of time, the plants in that area will flower earlier than the others. The pattern in this instance is telltale as the early flowering plants are immediately below the errant light.

Leaf spots can be caused by several different things. There are some diseases that infest mum foliage, but in the greenhouse these diseases are fairly rare. Possibly the most common cause of leaf troubles is the improper use of insecticides. A few of the insecticide chemicals cause leaf spots or burns and some of the materials that are used in mixing insecticides can be harmful. It is best to use a wettable powder rather than emulsions in greenhouses. Sometimes the trouble is caused by the operator's spraying with several materials at the same time. Foliar nematode can cause wedge shaped dead areas on mum leaves, but some of the other damage can appear rather wedge shaped too, and it may be confusing to make a decision based on just looking at the leaves.

Rose

Rose plants are planted in the spring of the year, and flower production starts in the summer and continues throughout the year until the plants are cut back the following summer. The plants usually are kept in the bench for four years, and they continue in constant flower production, except for the periods following the cutback, after the first and second year. The plants may or may not be cut back after the third year depending on when they are to be removed the following spring.

- ROSES CAN BE PROPAGATED BY BUDDING, GRAFTING, OR BY ROOTED CUTTINGS; HOWEVER, IT IS MOST COMMON TO USE BUDDING

Budding is the job of the specialist, and it is done in areas where the outdoor climate is favorable—California, Oregon, Arizona or Texas.

Rosa manetti is used for the root stock. This is a single-petalled rose variety used only because it forms a good root system for most greenhouse rose varieties. Hardwood cuttings of manetti are de-eyed—all but the top two buds are removed—and the cuttings are lined out in the field in December. By May the manetti plant is well established and budding commences. The soil is scraped away from the base of the manetti plant, the bark is cut, the bud from the greenhouse variety rose is inserted in the cut, and a tie is placed around the stem to hold the bud in place. For the plants that are budded from May to July the tops of the manetti plants are cut off just above the bud about three weeks after budding. The greenhouse

Fig. 6—34. Rose budder and tier at work in California rose field. The greenhouse variety bud is being placed on the manetti root stock. (Amling-DeVor Nurseries, Inc., photograph)

Fig. 6—35. A California field of rose started-eye plants. (Amling-DeVor Nurseries, Inc., photograph)

Fig. 6—36. Dormant, started-eye, rose plants being packed for shipment to the greenhouse operator. (Amling-DeVor Nurseries, Inc., photograph)

variety bud then starts in growth, producing the desired greenhouse plant on manetti roots. This type of plant is known as a started-eye rose plant. When the plants are mature in late fall they are dug, pruned, graded as to size, packed, and placed in refrigerated storage until shipment to the greenhouse rose grower from late December through the spring.

Manetti that is budded in late July and August is grown as dormant-eye plants. The tops of the manetti plants are not cut off after budding, and the greenhouse rose bud does not start in growth. The dormant-eye plants are dug in late fall when mature, and the manetti top then is cut off just above the dormant bud of the greenhouse variety.

Good greenhouse plants can be grown from either started-eye plants or from dormant-eye plants, but the started-eye plants are used more commonly. The XXX grade budded plant is the largest size, and it is considered the best to use. Excellent plants, however, can be grown from the XX grade.

Although budded plants can be obtained in late December, there seldom is an advantage in planting that early. Some refrigerated storage is beneficial to the budded plants, and weather conditions are better for the growth of the new plant after late January. If the plants are received before the time for planting, place them in 33° storage until a few days before the time to plant. Then open the boxes and inspect the plants. If there is no evidence of swelling or growth of the "eyes" keep the plants moist at 60° temperature until the "eyes" start to swell and break. This should not take more than a day or two, and this sweating-out period should not be continued until there is shoot growth on the plants.

Budded rose plants can be stored successfully until late spring if they are kept just above freezing. In fact, they can be stored longer than that with good results, but planting should be done before the hot weather of the summer unless the greenhouse is equipped with an air cooling and mist system.

Grafting is a greenhouse operation and the rose grower may graft only for his needs or he may graft some additional plants for sale. Since this is handled usually as an additional project by the existing crew, the grafting is scheduled for the period between Christmas and Easter when the crews are not occupied with other duties. Manetti plants are obtained from growers on the West Coast during the winter, and the grafting is done in February and March.

Usually the diameter of the root stock is greater than the diameter of the scion. This is no problem, but care must be taken to place the scion on the root stock so that the top of the cut edge of the scion

Fig. 6—37. The greenhouse variety rose scion has been placed on the manetti root stock with a bark graft. It will then be tied with a rubber band and placed in the grafting case. (Walter J. Engel, Inc., photograph)

Fig. 6—38. A rose grafting case showing the blocks used for supplying air gradually as the graft knits. (Walter J. Engel, Inc., photograph)

is exposed above the root stock and the bark of scion and root stock should be matched as closely as possible along one edge.

The purpose of the grafting case is to provide warm, moist surroundings suitable for the spliced ends of root stock and scion to grow together. The temperature in the case should be maintained at 75°, and the top is completely closed with glass panes to retain the moisture in the case. High humidity in the case is needed to prevent the cut edges of scion and root stock from drying out. After some callus forms on the upper union of scion and root stock, the glass panes can be opened gradually to allow some air movement in the case. It requires about one month in the grafting case for good union of scion and root stock, and more air is added daily until the case is completely uncovered at the end of this period.

Equally good results can be obtained by placing grafted plants in open benches if mist is properly supplied over the plants. The bench temperature should be 75° as in the grafting case and the mist supplied just often enough to keep the graft union moist. After callus starts to form at the top union of scion and root stock, the mist is gradually reduced. Generally the mist system of producing grafted plants can be operated more easily than the grafting case method.

After the plants are removed from the grafting case or from under the mist, they should be grown for a short period of time in the grafting pots and then knocked out and planted directly to the bench where they are going to be grown. Since grafted plants are in an active state of growth, they should be given the best growing conditions all the time. In many instances they are not planted soon enough, and the plants become hard. Growth is then slow and of poor quality after they are planted in the bench.

There is an old saying among rose growers that grafted plants do not make good producing plants until the second year. Too often this is true, but it is not due to the method of propagation. It is due to the mismanagement of that method. Grafted plants will be as good as or better than budded plants in the first year only if the young grafted plants are grown actively all the time. They need to be supplied fertilizer regularly, given adequate space and light, and kept free of pests. The two spotted mite is the most likely pest, and it can ruin young, grafted plants rapidly. It is not possible to keep the plants growing actively in the small grafting pots for longer than six to eight weeks after the grafts are made. The grafting schedule must be based on the planting date. Plants grafted March 1 need to be planted by April 15 to May 1.

Rooted cuttings can be used as a means of propagating roses, and this method is selected occasionally by the rose grower for his own use. Rose rooted cuttings are seldom produced for sale to another grower. If properly managed this is a very satisfactory method of rose propagation, and it probably should be practiced more. The same mismanagement problems exist with it as with grafted plants. If these can be avoided, excellent plants can be made from rooted cuttings. Rose rooted cuttings are called "own roots." This term emphasizes that the rooted cutting is on its own roots and the budded and grafted plants are on manetti roots. Two eye cuttings are used—the stem to be propagated is cut into sections each of which has two leaves—and at 60° air temperature and 70° bench temperature rooting takes place in four to five weeks. Perlite, coarse sand, or mixtures of perlite and peat are suitable for rooting roses, and a mist system should be used over the propagation bench. After rooting, the cuttings can be planted directly to the bench or potted. Surprisingly good results can be obtained from planting rose rooted cuttings directly to the bench where they will be grown. The cuttings will have much better light in the bench than when grown closely together in small pots, and they will be watered, fertilized, and pinched better. If the rooted cutting is potted, it then should be transplanted to the bench within three weeks after potting. One of the most common abuses of own roots is keeping them too long in small pots. They may not die in such a situation, but they do not grow well either. When they are finally transplanted to the bench the plants are hard, and they grow slowly and produce small diameter canes.

The schedule for rooting rose cuttings should be based on the planting time of the rooted cuttings. If the rooted cuttings are going to be planted directly to the bench, the cuttings should be stuck in the propagation bench about five weeks before the planting date. If the rooted cuttings are to be potted, the cuttings should be stuck in the propagation bench two months before the bench planting date. The propagation wood can be taken from the house that is to be replanted if the same varieties are wanted. This is a method for getting propagation wood without reducing the flower production in the greenhouse. The propagation wood can be gathered over quite a period of time as it can be stored satisfactorily in plastic bags at 33° for at least two weeks.

• PREPARE THE SOIL WELL FOR ROSES

Since rose plants remain in the same soil for about four years, it is very important to do an excellent job of soil preparation before planting. If planting is done during the dark and cold weather of January or February, especial care needs to be taken to be sure that the soil dries as quickly as possible after planting so that the new root growth is rapid. This can be promoted by using coarse, well drained soil; spot watering the plants—leaving dry areas between the plants; and operating the heating lines continuously around the benches that are planted.

A fertilizer application should be given with the first thorough watering after planting. A continuous supply of nitrogen is needed in the early stages of growth of the plant to produce large heavy stems.

• ROSES USE LARGE QUANTITIES OF FERTILIZER
IF SOIL DRAINAGE AND WATERING ARE GOOD

Superphosphate and calcium fertilizers invariably should be added to rose soils before planting. The best distribution of these fertilizers through the soil is obtained by incorporating them into the soil at the time that it is tilled and made ready for planting. The fertilizers then needed to be added regularly are nitrogen and potassium. A mixture of potassium nitrate and ammonium nitrate is a good fertilizer for regular liquid application. Organic fertilizers such as blood and tankage are used commonly on roses and, although they are not high analysis fertilizers, they are slowly available and provide some nitrogen over a long period of time. Rose plants grow rapidly and can use large amounts of nitrogen, particularly when they are in the leafy, vegetative stage of growth.

An application of iron fertilizer about once a year can be beneficial to roses. It is best to use Sequestrene 330 Fe at the rate of ¼ pound per 100 gallons of water, and applied at the rate of 1 quart per square foot of soil.

Rose soil should be watered heavily, and considerable labor is saved if an irrigation system is used. Pipe and nozzle systems located either in the middle of the bench or on each side are used successfully.

It is important to remember that budded plants are dormant before planting, but both grafted plants and own roots are actively growing plants—at least they should be. They need to be handled in such a way that the best growing conditions are provided for them at all times. Anything less than this is harmful to a plant at the time, as well as later in its growth. It is not possible to forget about or abuse the young plant in its early stages, and then attempt to produce an excellent plant by good care later on. The young plants must be fertilized and watered religiously and spaced adequately so that all parts of the plants get good sunlight. Plant the grafts and rooted cuttings to the bench as soon as possible, and then grow them as actively as possible.

In the early stages of growth of the rose plant the object is to develop several heavy shoots from the base of the plant. Very often one heavy shoot develops along with several thin to medium-weight shoots. The heavy shoot is no problem, but it probably is best to let it grow to the young bud stage and then pinch it to a 5-leaflet leaf. The other shoots should be pinched as soon as they can be handled. This is when they are only an inch or two long, and the tiny tip can be broken out above one or two 5-leaflet leaves that barely have started to unfold. When pinched at this stage the leaves immediately below the pinch expand the most, and the shoots that develop after this early pinch are heavier than the shoot that was pinched. This type of pinching develops good sized leaves and heavy shoots or canes on the young plant. This type of pinch can be used later on occasional shoots that are not as heavy as they should be.

- **ROSE PLANTS MUST BE GIVEN SOME SUPPORT TO KEEP THE PLANTS GROWING UPRIGHT**

In some instances 8-gauge metal stakes are placed by each plant and each individual stem is tied directly to the stake. This is a continual job as new ties must be added as the stems grow in length.

Fig. 6—39. Newly planted rose, started-bud plants covered with straw to keep uniformly moist conditions around the canes. Other means of supplying moist surroundings for the newly planted roses are to use hot caps over the plants or support plastic film over the entire bed. Any of these coverings need to be removed promptly as the plants start to break, and the plants should be misted periodically during the day.

Fig. 6—40. The eyes just starting to break on a newly planted started-eye rose. At this stage the covering must be removed from the plants, and light misting should be given several times a day.

During harvest, first the strings are cut that hold the stem to the stake and then the flower is cut. The other method of support is much the same as the support that is used for carnations, except that a 2-foot metal stake is used by each plant to get the stems started upright and then the first grid of wire and string starts about 1 foot above the soil. Additional grids are placed about 1 foot apart and the stems are

Fig. 6—41. Rose stems and the position of pinch or cut. Left to right: this stem is small, but it is the best stage for making an early pinch. The pinch removes the tip just above two 5-leaflet leaves as they are unfolding; the soft pinch is made on rose shoots at about this stage above the first or second 5-leaflet leaf. The soft pinch is used for timing flower production for a certain time of year — the flower is produced 5 to 8 weeks after the pinch is made depending on the time of the year; in the fall and early winter the flower is cut above two 5-leaflet leaves.

"poked" into the upright columns formed by these grids. Either support system can be used, depending on which one works in better.

• ROSE SOILS ARE MULCHED WITH STRAWY MANURE, CORN COBS, STRAW OR HAY

New mulch is added several times during the year. This helps to keep the soil in good physical condition, maintains more uniform soil moisture, and adds some nutrients to the soil. It is also quite possible that the mulch helps maintain the carbon dioxide level in the greenhouse during the day.

● ROSES ARE A 60° CROP AND DO BEST AT HIGH HUMIDITY

Night temperatures in the rose house should be maintained at 60° and day temperatures at 65° to 70° depending on whether the day is cloudy or clear. Plant growth and flowering are faster in warm temperatures, and sometimes before a holiday the temperature is raised or lowered gradually to speed or delay the crop as necessary.

Houses that are furnished with high pressure mist systems are ideal for roses. Mist reduces the temperature during the summer and adds moisture to the air at any time of the year. High humidity can produce larger leaves, longer stems, and larger flowers. Before automatic, high pressure mist systems were available roses were syringed regularly by hand. Actually this was a two phase program—to make the surroundings more moist and to wash two spotted mites off the leaves. Syringing was an excellent practice and still can be, but it had one unfavorable effect—it was quite efficient at distributing and propagating the black spot disease throughout the house. When miticides were developed that controlled the two spotted mite, syringing was decreased and black spot of greenhouse roses became almost an unknown disease.

● ROSES ARE CROPPED BY PINCHING

In most areas of the country the Christmas, Valentine, Easter, and Mother's Day markets are good for roses. Many rose growers increase the crop for these holidays by pinching the plants the right length of time before the holiday. Depending on the time of the year and the weather conditions, it requires five to eight weeks for a flower to develop after the stem is pinched. This is an entirely different type of pinch than the early pinch used for building the plant. It is called a soft pinch, and it is done by pinching just above the first or second 5-leaflet leaf from the tip of the stem. For many areas the Christmas pinch is made the last week in October, the Valentine pinch the middle of December (sometimes the return crop from the Christmas cut makes Valentine's Day), an early Easter may require the pinch eight weeks before and a late Easter six weeks before, and the Mother's Day pinch is made about five weeks before.

- **THERE ARE TWO TYPES OF ROSES GROWN IN THE GREENHOUSE**

The large flowered types are Hybrid Tea roses. The small flowered types are classed as Floribundas, and they commonly are called Sweetheart roses. There is not much side shoot development on the Hybrid Teas, but if there are side shoots, they are removed so there is just one flower per stem. Some Sweetheart varieties form side shoots, and these may be allowed to flower as a spray of flowers per stem. However, many of the more popular Sweetheart varieties have one flower per stem.

In Hybrid Tea roses, red is the most popular color. Quite often red accounts for more than 75% of the total production. The variety Better Times was the predominant red variety grown for over thirty years following its introduction in 1929. It is a good grower and producer. It has been replaced by varieties that are truer reds and have improved keeping qualities,—largely by Yuletide, Happiness, Red American Beauty, and Forever Yours. The next most popular Hybrid Tea color is yellow, followed by pink with white next. With Floribundas light pink is the color most in demand, followed by red, yellow, white and other colors. Floribundas have increased in favor primarily because of their excellent keeping quality. A grower might have around 10% of his area planted to Floribundas; however, since the Floribunda production is nearly twice that of the Hybrid Teas, the quantity of flowers produced would be greater than 10%.

- **ROSE FLOWERS DEVELOP RAPIDLY AND THE FLOWERS ARE CUT TWICE A DAY, EVERY DAY**

Depending on the variety, some are cut in the tight bud stage and others after they just start to unfurl. As roses are sold by stem length, it is desired to cut as long a stem as possible. Of even more importance, however, is the effect that the place of cut will have on the plant and the following crops. Deep cutting is not done during the fall as this would remove too many leaves from the plant for good growth during the winter. In the spring deep cutting can be practiced as good weather conditions at that time of the year produce good plant growth. The general practice is to cut to two 5-leaflet leaves during the fall and winter. The plant then increases in height with each cut and good leaves are left on the plant. Starting in late February the stem is cut to the first 5-leaflet leaf below the previous cut or "cut below the hook."

Generally it is found that rose production and quality are improved if the plants are "grown up" (grown taller). This is done by

Fig. 6—42. In the fall and early winter the rose is cut above two 5-leaflet leaves as indicated by the stem on the left. This method of cutting allows the plant to increase in height, and good leaves are maintained on the plant. Starting in late winter the rose is cut below the hook. This gives quite an increase in stem length on the flower even after the hook is removed. On the stem to the right the hook portion is just below the bottom leaf. Because of the good growing conditions during the spring deep cutting like this can be done without seriously affecting the growth or production of the plant.

not cutting as deep or by alternating a pinch with a cut. In some instances the plants are so tall that the cutters wear stilts or walk the side of the bench to cut the flowers.

In spite of the best laid plans some of the canes on the plant will not be as heavy as desired. Continuing to cut flowers from such canes will result in thinner and shorter stems on the flowers. These thin

Fig. 6—43. Flowers must be placed in water as soon as possible after cutting and then refrigerated. Roses particularly must be placed in water quickly, and there should be buckets or trays right in the greenhouses for this purpose.

canes either should be removed from the plant entirely or the shoots that develop from them should be pinched in the very early stage. The early pinch will produce maximum sized leaves, and the shoot that follows will be heavier.

Keep in mind that the best effect from the early pinch is realized when it is made early—when the shoot is only about an inch long and the tip is pinched out above the first two 5-leaflet leaves just as they are unfolding.

A look at the stem from which the shoot arises will tell you whether to make the early pinch or not. If the stem is not as heavy as you would like, make the early pinch and the result will be a heavier stem. If two or three shoots develop after a stem is cut, the first shoot invariably will be the heaviest and longest. Some early pinching of the second and third shoots should be done continually to maintain good quality canes on the plant.

After cutting, the flowers are placed in water, then graded and bunched and placed in water in the refrigerator. The following morning they are taken or shipped to the market. Roses are graded by stem length—usually in increments of 3 inches. On some markets roses below 15 inches are classed as utility or work roses. The standard bunch is 25 flowers; however, in some instances they may be packed 12 or 13 to the bunch.

- **BY ONE METHOD OR THE OTHER, ROSE PLANTS NEED TO BE CUT BACK EACH YEAR**

If they were not cut back, they would become too tall to handle conveniently. If cutting below the hook is done regularly in the spring, the plants will be pretty well cut back by summer. If this has not reduced the height of the plants enough, they then are cut back to about two feet in late spring or during the summer. The cut back plant then is handled in much the same way as starting the new plant. The first shoots are given an early pinch, since the object is to develop good, heavy canes on the plant.

- **THE MOST PERSISTENT PEST ON ROSES IS THE TWO SPOTTED MITE (RED SPIDER)**

It is usually on the under side of the leaf, and it starts most often on the lower foliage. This pest requires continual and thorough treatment to keep it under control.

Thrips in season can be a problem. They inhabit the flowers, and the results of their work are more obvious than the pests themselves. They cause crippling of the flower buds, cupping of the petals, and streaks on the petals. Thrips sail into the greenhouse from outdoor crops, and since this is a continual process, treatment needs to be almost continuous. The thrips season is in late May or June and again in late summer.

Aphids are found on roses occasionally, usually on the stem tips. They are rather easy to see and should be treated promptly. Control of aphids is not difficult on roses.

- **POWDERY MILDEW IS A CONSTANT THREAT TO ROSES**

It is readily recognized by the powdery, white growth on the leaves and the cupping or crippling of the leaves. Powdery mildew is most common from spring through fall, although it is possible to have

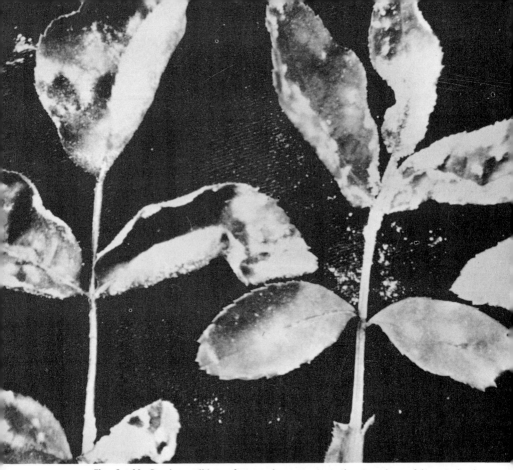

Fig. 6—44. Powdery mildew of roses is a constant threat and careful control of temperatures and ventilation is needed to prevent it. (From Kodachrome by C. W. Ellett)

an infestation at any time. Apparently the spores of this fungus are everpresent in the greenhouse air, and they start growth readily when there is a slight film of moisture on the leaves. During the heating season the most critical times of the day are at sunup and sundown. The source of heat shifts at these times from the sun to the steam pipes or vice versa. If the steam does not start to take over the job of warming the plants before the sun fails in the afternoon, and if the steam does not continue to warm the plants until the sun is well up in the morning and handling the job, the leaves can cool just enough for moisture to deposit on them. Start heating in the afternoon well before the sun wanes, and continue heating in the morning until the sun is up. At both times of the day it should be necessary to do some ventilating while heating to maintain the right air temperature. In warm weather it is possible to have humid and stagnant conditions that are ideal for the start of the disease. Continual air circulation by properly placed air circulation fans is helpful.

Sulfur is a standard control for powdery mildew. During the heating season it is vaporized from the steam lines at least three times a week for good control. In some instances electrically-heated sulfur pots are used, and these have the advantage that they can be used at any time of the year. Other chemicals for control of powdery mildew are Karathane and Actidione PM.

● PROBLEMS ARISE RAPIDLY WITH ROSE PLANTS

The rose is a fast grower, and turns for the worse develop as fast as improvements. In spite of the problems and the speed with which they can appear, the rose is a very rewarding plant with which to work as it shows the results of good treatment readily, also.

Leaf drop is a perennial problem with roses, and it seems that just about anything can be the cause for leaf drop. This, of course, is a real problem as food for the plant is manufactured in the leaves, and when the leaves drop, the food supply in the plant is decreased. It is the older leaves toward the bottom of the plant that drop, but it is not unusual to find the canes bare of leaves for two to three feet above the soil. Leaf drop is much more likely during the poor light conditions of the winter. Any damage to the roots or poor root growth associated with poor drainage, over-watering, too much fertilizer, or pest damage can cause leaf drop. Insecticides and fungicides or a combination of them often cause leaf drop.

Bullhead is the term used for malformed rose flowers involving some crippled petals and a short and often lopsided bud. Thrips can cause bullheads, and this is one of the first signs of an infestation during the thrips season. Some insecticides have caused bullheads, and there seems to be a relationship with rate of growth. Very vigorous shoots often bullhead.

Blind wood or blindness refers to rose stems that do not develop flowers. The cause of blind wood is not known although several things have been suspected. Blind wood seems to occur mostly on weaker growth, and it is likely that much of it is eliminated if early pinching is really practiced. Blind wood is either cut out or pinched. There is

Fig. 6—45. The flower on the left is a well-developed rose. The one on the right is called a bullhead. The petals are shorter and the bud is not uniform.

some indication that the addition of carbon dioxide to the greenhouse air reduces blind wood.

Several nematodes can infest roses. It is fairly easy to distinguish the presence of root knot nematodes by the knots that they cause on the roots. The presence of other kinds is not so obvious on the roots. With any of the nematode infestations the top growth of the plants is poor. The leaves are small and the shoots short. The leaf color is pale and dull. Seek the help of an expert to identify the trouble. Rose plants can be treated successfully by using 2 gallons of Nemagon 2 E.C. per acre of soil followed by a heavy watering. Two applications should be made about six months apart.

Nematodes may be introduced by soil or mulch that is used for the roses, or they may be brought in with the budded or grafted plants. One of the advantages in using own root plants is that they should be free of nematodes if normal care is used.

Do not use mercury thermometers or mercury based fungicides in rose houses. Mercury vapors are toxic to roses, and cause leaf drop, discoloration of flowers, petal drop, and stunted growth. Trouble has resulted also from paint containing a mercury fungicide.

Snapdragon

Snapdragons are propagated from seed. They may be grown at any time of the year, but the greatest flower production is from mid-December through May. Most commonly they are grown as single stem plants, and the plants are discarded after the flowers are cut.

In some situations it is desired to take a second crop from the plants. When this is done the plants are left in place after cutting, and as the shoots develop they are pruned to two per plant. Snapdragons can be grown as pinched plants. They are given a soft pinch three weeks after planting, and the shoots that develop are pruned to three or four shoots per plant.

- SNAPDRAGON SEED IS SMALL AND IT MUST BE SOWN RIGHT
  AT THE SURFACE OF THE SEED FLAT

The seed is packed 2,000 seeds per trade packet, and it is planned to get 800 good seedlings from a packet of seed.

Damping-off diseases are very common in snapdragon seed flats. The flats and soil must be carefully steam sterilized; the seed should be sown thin enough so that air can circulate freely around the seedlings; and the maximum amount of air circulation should be provided. If the seed flat is covered to keep the surface moist, some air should be given as soon as germination starts and then increased as rapidly as possible without causing undue drying of the surface. Germination of snapdragon seeds under mist is good as the flat can be kept uniformly moist, and at the same time good air circulation can be maintained. If any damping-off is noticed, the flat and plants can be drenched with either Morsodren or a mixture of Dexon and Terraclor.

At 60° the seedlings should be ready for transplanting about four weeks after sowing. The snapdragon definitely should be transplanted

Fig. 6—46. Snapdragon seedlings at the right stage of growth for transplanting to the bench where they will be grown. The earlier they can be planted the better the growth of the plant will be.

as soon as it can be handled, and that is when the plants are only about an inch high and the first set of true leaves is just forming.

In planting, the young seedlings should be handled by their leaves. They are more easily handled this way, and there is less chance of damaging the stem. For flowering during the winter (Dec. 15-Mar. 15) single-stem plants are spaced 4 inches by 6 inches, for summer flowering (July 1-Sep. 1) they are planted 4 inches by 4 inches, for flowering during the fall and spring they are spaced 4 inches by 5 inches. Pinched plants are spaced about 8 inches by 8 inches, and they are pinched about three weeks after planting and then pruned to four stems.

Welded wire fabric makes an excellent support for snapdragons, and if varieties of about the same height are used in the bench, a single layer of the fabric is enough. This is the same type of support system that is used for chrysanthemums.

• USE A POROUS, WELL-DRAINED SOIL FOR SNAPDRAGONS

Snapdragons are sensitive to poorly drained soil. Be sure that the soil is well aerated, which is most easily done by having perfect drainage through the bottom of the bench and using a coarse, porous soil. A coarse soil will have good aeration and good growth of snapdragon roots even when it is well watered. Snapdragons are very easily overwatered in heavy, fine soil. Use straw, strawy manure, poultry litter peat, or peanut hulls in the soil, and then spade by hand rather than using a mechanical tiller.

If phosphorus and calcium fertilizers are added to the soil before planting, fertilizers containing only nitrogen and potassium can be used during the growth of the crop. Snapdragons do not require large amounts of fertilizer. They do well if they are fertilized with each watering by an injector. If this cannot be done, nitrogen and potassium should be applied every three to four weeks.

• USE THE RIGHT VARIETY FOR THE SEASON OF THE YEAR

Snapdragons will flower at any season of the year, but growth and flowering are much more rapid in bright, hot weather than in the dark, cool portion of the year. During the summer it may require less than three months for a crop to flower after planting, but during the winter it may take as long as five months. Unusually bright and warm weather advances the flowering of snapdragons, and cool dark weather delays flowering. The time of flowering can vary two to three weeks depending on the weather conditions at the time.

Actually, different varieties are used depending on the time of the year. Summer varieties would flower very slowly if at all during the winter, and winter varieties would flower very rapidly during the summer but on very short stems. Because of their suitability for the flowering period, snapdragon varieties are classified as winter varieties for flowering from Dec. 15 to Mar. 15; late winter, Apr. 1 to May 1; spring, May 15 to June 15; summer, July 1 to Sep. 1; fall, Sep. 15 to Oct. 15; and late fall, Nov. 1 to Dec. 1. Actually these are only four classifications of varieties as the same varieties are used for the late fall and late spring periods, and the same varieties are used for the spring and fall periods. Breeders of snapdragons have made considerable progress in developing new varieties. The F-1 hybrids are used almost exclusively, and there are high quality varieties for each of the flowering periods of the year.

- SNAPDRAGONS CAN BE GROWN THE YEAR AROUND
  OR ROTATED WITH OTHER CROPS

Since snapdragons require from three to five months in the bench and can be grown at any time of the year, they can be rotated with other crops when the time is available. A convenient rotation with carnations can be used in which fall-planted snaps are followed with carnations in the early spring, or possibly two crops of snaps are followed by carnations planted in late spring. Rotations with chrysanthemums can be worked out also.

For year-around flowering of snapdragons a 9-unit area would provide for flowering of single-stem snapdragons at 50° every week to two weeks throughout the year. The following schedule gives a possible rotation. Since it requires about one month for producing the seedling after sowing, the seed should be sowed about one month before each of the planting dates listed.

SAMPLE ROTATION FOR A 9-UNIT AREA IN SINGLE-STEM SNAPDRAGONS

	1st Crop		2nd Crop		3rd Crop	
Unit	Plant	Flower	Plant	Flower	Plant	Flower
1	Sep. 4	Jan. 1	Jan. 15	May 15	May 25	Aug. 1
2	Sep. 7	Jan. 15	Jan. 25	May 22	June 5	Aug. 15
3	Sep. 15	Feb. 1	Feb. 10	June 1	June 15	Aug. 22
4	Sep. 20	Feb. 15	Feb. 25	June 8	July 1	Sep. 1
5	Oct. 3	Mar. 1	Mar. 10	June 15	July 10	Sep. 15
6	Oct. 15	Mar. 15	Apr. 1	June 22	July 15	Sep. 22
7	Nov. 1	Apr. 1	Apr. 10	July 1	July 25	Oct. 1
8	Nov. 20	Apr. 15	May 1	July 15	Aug. 1	Oct. 15
9	Dec. 15	May 1	May 10	July 22	Aug. 10	Nov. 1

- TEMPERATURES FOR SNAPDRAGONS

The winter, late fall, and late winter varieties should be grown at 50° night temperature and 55° to 60° during the day depending on whether it is cloudy or bright. The summer, spring, and fall varieties are grown at 60° nights and 65° to 70° days.

Actually young snapdragon plants should be grown at 60° night temperature regardless of the variety classification as the growth is more rapid and of better quality than at the lower temperature. Very often this cannot be done, however, because the young plants are in the same house as the other plants that need to be grown at 50°.

• CUTTING AND SHIPPING SNAPDRAGONS

The lower florets of the snapdragon expand first, and the florets at the tip last. The flower should be cut before the tip florets are fully

Fig. 6—47. The snapdragon flower has a spike arrangement of florets. The lower florets develop first, and the flower should be cut at the stage when the bottom floret is well developed but still in good condition, and the top buds are still tightly folded.

expanded. At this stage the lower florets should still be in good condition. The stem is cut just above the soil, the flowers are graded by stem length, bunched in dozens, and placed in water in the refrigerator overnight.

There is a particular problem in shipping snapdragons. If they are placed in a horizontal position for a period of time, the stem tips bend upward (geotropism). Most customers like their snapdragons straight, and that means that they must be shipped and stored in an upright position. This effect can be observed also in arrangements if the designer places either snapdragons or gladioli on the horizontal in arrangements.

- **THE MOST SERIOUS SNAPDRAGON TROUBLES ARISE IN THE SOIL**

Snapdragons are quite susceptible to Pythium and Rhizoctonia, particularly in the early stages of growth. Soil, seed flats, benches, and handling equipment all must be carefully sterilized before use with snapdragons. The surface of the seed flats must be kept uniformly moist until germination, but as soon as possible be sure to provide continuous air movement around the flat. After planting, the plants should be carefully watered, particularly in the winter. Spot water the plants, leaving dry areas between plants, then let the soil dry somewhat before the next watering. Porous soil with good drainage is a definite help. Drench seed flats and newly transplanted plants with Morsodren or a combination of Dexon and Terraclor. In drenching be sure to get some of the drench on the base of the plants. Provide good ventilation in the house at all times; air circulation fans are a definite aid.

Botrytis stem rot is fairly common on older plants. It should be controlled if good ventilation and air circulation are maintained.

Aphids are the most common pests on snapdragons. They usually inhabit the tips of the plant, and if they are controlled in the early stages should not be a problem.

Floret drop is not nearly the problem it once was as so many of the varieties have been bred to be resistant to it. The two main causes are pollination by bees and ethylene gas given off from fruits, vegetables, or flowers stored in refrigerators. The bees can be eliminated by screening the ventilators, and the ethylene gas problem does not exist if the snapdragons are stored in the right environment.

Floret skip refers to the absence of florets here and there on the spike. This is not a common problem, and it seems to be associated primarily with the use of unusually cool temperatures.

Yellow or chlorotic tip leaves—usually on young plants—are caused by poor root growth or root damage. The poor root growth is most often caused by poor soil drainage, too heavy or fine soil, or too much fertilizer in the soil.

CHAPTER 7

Pot Plant Crops

CHAPTER 7

Some pot plant crops are produced the year around, but many of them are grown only at one season. The pot plant grower may have a rotation of crops consisting of poinsettias for Christmas, azaleas for spring, lilies for Easter, hydrangeas and chrysanthemums for Easter and Mother's Day, and chrysanthemums for summer. Such a rotation can keep the greenhouse space fully occupied throughout the year; and it does provide the desired assortment of plants at all seasons.

Pot plants are grown on raised benches and very often they are wide benches as 6-foot to 8-foot benches can be worked from each side conveniently for pot plants. Since there must be considerable movement of pot plants from the potting room to the benches and then to the shipping area, much time and effort can be saved if these areas are close and accessible to wheeled vehicles.

• A GOOD SOURCE OF SOIL IS NEEDED FOR POT PLANTS

Pot plant soil cannot be re-used. It is sold along with the plant. The pot plant grower needs to have a dependable source of good soil. If he does not have enough acreage himself, he has to obtain the soil from construction or road building projects. Of course only top soil can be used, and even this needs to be chosen wisely. Switching soil types also will necessitate changes in the other materials that are added to the soil before potting. The acidity may need to be adjusted, more or different fertilizer may be needed, and the amount of organic matter to be added may need to be changed. Soils vary considerably even in the same locality, and it is not safe to assume that the same kind of soil will be delivered with each load. Chemical weed killers are being used commonly on much land. Some of these chemicals are not toxic to the field crop, but they may be toxic to your greenhouse

Fig. 7—1. Do not fill the pot completely with soil. About half of the width of the lip of the pot should be freeboard so that enough water can be applied at a time to thoroughly wet all of the soil in the pot.

crop. Determine what chemicals have been used on the soil before you obtain it for your pot plants.

It is very unusual if a soil can be taken right from the field and used successfully for growing pot plants in the greenhouse. Most field soils need some coarse organic matter or coarse aggregate added to them before they will be porous enough to drain freely in greenhouse conditions. Field soils commonly are deficient in phosphorus and calcium, so superphosphate and some form of calcium fertilizer should be added as the potting soil is mixed.

In some areas of the country it is customary to make soil mixtures without soil—using peat moss plus sand, perlite, or vermiculite. These mixtures are light in weight, and it is possible to reproduce the same mixture each time. Fertilizers do need to be added at the time of mixing as they are entirely devoid of fertilizer to start with, and the fertilizer program after planting needs to be carefully worked out to assure that all the fertilizer materials that are needed are supplied. The basic requirements for the potting mixtures are the same as for soil mixtures—they must drain freely, they must not dry too rapidly, and they must have an adequate fertilizer supply.

● CLAY POTS, PLASTIC POTS, PEAT POTS

The standard greenhouse flower pot is as high as it is wide—a 6-inch standard pot is 6 inches wide and 6 inches high. Azalea pots are three fourths as high as they are wide, and bulb pans are half as high as they are wide. Other special pots are made, but these are the most common types in use. In spite of the name, the "azalea" pot is used quite commonly for pot chrysanthemums, and poinsettias usually are panned in either "azalea" pots or "bulb" pans.

Clay, plastic, and peat pots all have some good features and the choice of pot should be based on which one can be used most successfully in the specific situation. Clay pots have been used for years. They are porous, and it is generally felt that there is some advantage in the exchange of air and moisture through the wall of the pot. Clay pots are heavy, and particularly if the pot plants are to be

Fig. 7—2. From left to right: standard 6-inch clay pot; 6-inch azalea clay pot; 6-inch azalea plastic pot; 3-inch clay peat pot; 3-inch round peat pot; and 3-inch square peat pot.

shipped, the weight of the pot may be a consideration. Algae grow well on the outside of clay pots, and this green or black growth can make them rather unsightly. The outside of the pot should be cleaned before the pot plant is shipped out.

Plastic pots are lightweight, and algae do not grow well on them. However, the plastic is not porous, and neither air nor moisture is exchanged through the wall of the pot. Because of the light weight and ease in cleaning them, plastic pots are used in many instances. The soil in plastic pots does not dry as rapidly as it does in clay pots, and the soil mixture should be more porous. It is possible to over-water soil in plastic pots more easily than soil in clay pots.

Peat pots are used only in the smaller sizes as transplanting pots—pot as well as plant is planted. Depending on how they are used, equally good growth can be obtained with either clay or peat pots. In some instances the peat pots can be handled more easily, and the need for sterilization of pot before use each time is eliminated. The peat pots, however, cannot be handled individually after potting, and they are placed in racks, baskets, or boxes so that several can be picked up and moved at a time. The roots of the plant should grow through the walls of the peat pot. At the time of transplanting the walls of the pot should be moist, and the plant should be watered well afterwards so there is good contact between the pot and the surrounding soil.

- **THE POTTING ROOM NEEDS TO BE ARRANGED SO THAT THE WORK IS DONE MOST EFFICIENTLY**

Storage areas for pots, soil, peat, manure and fertilizer need to be provided. The soil, manure, used pots, flats, and handling equipment must be steam sterilized before use. This is done usually in a chest close to the potting room.

The potting table is about 5 feet deep and has a backboard on it so that soil can be piled against it and mixed. To mix potting soil by hand the soil, manure, peat, and fertilizer or other ingredients are placed in a pile on the potting table. Using a straight-edged shovel and starting at one edge of the pile, the shovel is loaded by pushing it forward on the table all the way to the backboard. It is then tipped on edge away from the pile as it is drawn back, and the shovelful is distributed across the width of the table. This is called "turning" and the entire pile is "turned" to the left and then to the right. The direction of the turn—to right or left—is reversed each time. It is necessary to turn the pile three or four times to get complete mixing. Potting soil should be moist—not wet nor dry. If peat is used in the soil mixture it may need to be soaked for some time before use, as dry peat absorbs water slowly.

For a right-handed person it is best to arrange the potting table with the rooted cuttings or plants on the left, the empty pots in front of the soil pile, and a place for the potted plant to the right. For small pots the pot is filled by shoving it into the soil pile with the right hand while picking up the plant with the left. With finger or dibble a hole is made in the soil, the plant is placed in the hole, the thumbs and forefingers of both hands are used to compress the soil on each side of the plant in one motion, and the pot is set in a flat to the right.

For potting in larger pots a piece of broken pot, a plastic chip, or coarse gravel is placed over the hole in the bottom of the pot to improve the drainage. A handful or two of soil is placed in the pot with the right hand, and while the plant is held in the pot with the left hand, more soil is filled in around the plant with the right hand. The soil is firmed around the plant with a single motion of thumbs and forefingers of both hands. The pot must not be completely filled with soil. There must be a freeboard of at least half the width of the lip of the pot. This allows enough water to be put on to wet the soil thoroughly.

While the potting is being done be sure the roots of the cuttings or young plants are not allowed to dry, and the potted plants should be moved to the greenhouse bench as soon as possible and watered thoroughly. The pots must be set perfectly level on the bench, or it will not be possible to water them properly. They should be set in straight lines, too. This not only gives a more orderly appearance, but it will be easier to work with the plants later.

• THE GRADUAL SHIFT AND DIRECT POTTING

There was a time when small plants were potted only in small pots, then shifted from one size pot to the next larger size until it was finally potted in the finish pot. This is known as the gradual shift, and there are certain advantages in using it. It is difficult to over-water a plant in a small pot, and root growth can be faster. The problems with the gradual shift are greater than the benefits, however. If the plant is not shifted to the next pot soon enough, growth of the plant can be hard and stunted. Small pots may not be spaced soon enough, and as a result the plant may not receive enough sunlight. There is considerable labor involved in the gradual shift, and this is the main reason why it is not used.

Potting the young plant directly to the pot in which it is to be finished requires the least labor, but it does use the maximum space. There may be problems in getting small plants established in large pots. The soil in that large volume may dry slowly, and the root growth may be slow. It requires more care and skill by the grower to get young plants started in large pots.

A single shift is the best compromise. Start the young plant in either a 2¼-inch or 3-inch pot, then shift it to the finish pot. The small pot gives a fast start, and the single shift does not require much labor.

• GIVE THE POTTED PLANTS PLENTY OF SPACE

Since potted plants can be moved, it is possible to space them closely together when the plants are small and then space them out as the plants grow. This is a method of conserving space but it does consume labor, and unless the plants are spaced out soon enough the quality of the plant is hurt. The pot plant grower needs to have a definite plan for space requirements on each crop. Some growers set the plants at the finish spacing at the start, and they believe that the improvement in plant quality and the saving in labor pay for the extra space that is used.

• WATERING AND FERTILIZING SYSTEMS ARE A BIG AID IN GROWING PLANTS

There are several versions of the small-diameter plastic tube method of watering pot plants. These systems provide a method of applying water to each pot with a minimum of labor, and they probably can be used on any pot plant crop to good advantage.

It is virtually impossible to distribute dry fertilizer evenly on pot plants, and this method requires considerable labor time, as well. The best method of applying fertilizer to pot plants is with a fertilizer injector. The fertilizer is then supplied with each watering, and the plants' needs are taken care of with the minimum of labor. The injector can be used also with the plastic tube irrigation system.

- **THE POT PLANT GROWER SHOULD SPEND AS MUCH TIME LOOKING AT THE ROOTS AS HE DOES AT THE TOPS OF THE PLANTS**

He has a wonderful opportunity to do this, too, as it is an easy task to knock the plant out of the pot to inspect the roots. This is done by placing the right hand over the soil in the pot, inverting the plant, and with the left hand on the pot, striking the lip of the pot on the edge of the bench. The pot comes free from the soil and the plant is inverted in the right hand with full view of the roots—or lack of roots.

Fig. 7—3. It is very important to keep track of root growth on plants at all times. For pot plants invert the plant with one hand over the soil, and the plant then comes loose from the pot when the rim of the pot is tapped on the edge of the bench.

Fig. 7—4. Inspecting the roots on a pot mum. Plant must be carefully knocked out of the pot for the first week or so after potting or the soil may crumble. After root growth starts the soil ball holds together well.

Fig. 7—5. Concrete blocks on end make suitable legs for pot plant benches, and 2-inch by 4-inch wooden cross members are used between the legs. Note the well spaced bottom boards to provide good drainage.

Fig. 7—6. Pot plant benches must drain well and allow good air circulation around the plants. The boards in this bench bottom are well spaced.

For the first two weeks after potting, the plants must be knocked out carefully as the soil ball may split.

If the root growth is good, this verifies that the soil mixture is satisfactory, drainage through the soil is good, watering practices have been all right, and there is not too much fertilizer in the soil. If the root system is good, but the top growth not as good as could be expected, it is most likely that the fertilization program is at fault. Increase in top growth could be expected from the use of the right fertilizers. If the roots are not growing well, good root growth will have to be established before any improvement in the top of the plant can be expected.

- **THE POINSETTIA IS NOT WORTH A NICKEL THE DAY AFTER CHRISTMAS**

There is occasional sale for holiday plants after the holiday, but very often the plants that flower too late are a complete loss. Timing of holiday pot plants is difficult and a big worry. Lily growers sometimes kid each other about the pots being worn thin on the bottom from being moved from a house of one temperature to a house of another temperature to slow or speed the time of flowering. The time of flowering of most holiday crops varies with the weather, and the weather has a way of being just a bit different from year to year. It is not known three months or six months before the holiday if this is going to be a bright or a dull season. Easter is an especial challenge in timing. It may be as early as late March or as late as late April. The weather conditions can be entirely different for an early Easter than they are for a late Easter, and the growing schedule must take this into account.

• POT PLANTS ARE SOLD BY POT SIZE

Although varying with different crops, most pot plants are referred to by the pot size. Of course, larger plants are usually in larger pots, but this is not always true. A 6-inch pot mum refers to a mum plant in a 6-inch pot. This does not necessarily describe the size of the plant except that plants in a given sales area are sized about the same for each size pot.

• POT PLANT ROTATIONS MUST BE CAREFULLY DEVELOPED

The pot plant grower's problem in developing a rotation is more complex than that of the cut flower grower. Cut flower plants are planted in a fixed amount of space and remain that way for the duration of the crop, which may be from several months to a few years. The pot plant grower is blessed—or bedevilled—by pots that can be moved, and theoretically the pot plants are spaced as the young plants grow into big plants. It takes some careful figuring to keep the entire area full at all times and yet have enough space for each plant when it needs it. If the pot plant grower produces only pot mums the year around in about the same quantity each week, his problem in allotting space should not be difficult. The grower who produces several different crops throughout the year is the one who must do some figuring to be sure of space at the right time.

A few problems can be illustrated by considering the space requirements for some of the typical holiday crops.

SPACE REQUIREMENTS IN SQUARE FEET FOR HOLIDAY CROPS IN A GREENHOUSE WITH 20,000 SQ. FT. OF BENCH SPACE

Month	Chrysanthemum						Poinsettia	Azalea			Lily	Hydrangea		Total
	Tha.	Chr.	Val.	Eas.	Mot.	Dec.	Chr.	Chr.	Val.	Eas.	Eas.	Eas.	Mot.	
Jan.			1000	700					4000		2000	500		6200
Feb.				1000	3000				4000		3000	1000	150	12150
Mar.				2000	4000	500				1000	7000	3000	250	17750
Apr.				3000	4000	1500				1000	8000	4000	500	22000
May					15000	2000	800						2200	20000
June							1000							1000
July							1600							1600
Aug.							3100							3100
Sep.	1000						2000							3000
Oct.	2700	600					5000							8300
Nov.	4000	1800	200				12000	2000						20000
Dec.		2500	500				15000	2000						20000

Key to holiday abbreviations:

Tha.	Thanksgiving
Chr.	Christmas
Val.	Valentine's Day
Eas.	Easter
Mot.	Mother's Day
Dec.	Decoration Day

In this 20,000 square foot pot plant range (30,000 square feet under glass—20,000 square feet in bench area and 10,000 square feet in walks and work area) the following numbers of pot plants would be forced for the holidays:

Holiday	Mums 6"	Azalea 6"	Poinsettia 6"	7"	8"	Lily 6"	Hydrangea 6"
Tha.	2700						
Chr.	1700	2000	8000	1000	300		
Val.	700	4000					
Eas.	2000	1000				8000	2000
Mot.	10000						1100
Dec.	1400						

It is easy to see from the total column that much of the available space would not be occupied during the summer months, and more space than is available should be used in April. This is a fairly common situation. The market for holiday plants in the spring is good and there is a natural tendency to grow more plants than available space will hold. When Easter is late it is difficult to produce all of the plants that are needed for Mother's Day with adequate space for each plant. Therefore the plants do not get spaced out as they should and the quality of the Mother's Day plants is not as good as it should be. With an early Easter there is a problem in getting the poinsettias out of the benches fast enough so that the lilies and hydrangeas can be started.

Pot plant rotations must be developed for the specific situation. Crops can be handled successfully by different methods, and the space requirements will not necessarily be exactly the same as the ones in this example. Mums in 6-inch pots, if placed pot to pot, at first will require about 1 square foot for three pots. They are spaced as the plants grow, and they should be finished at about 1½ square feet per pot. As the Thanksgiving pot mums are sold the Christmas pot mums are given more space. The Mother's Day pot mums should be spaced out in the benches vacated by Easter pot mums, but too often this is giving them space too late.

The space required by poinsettias illustrates the need for planning for the size of the finished plant. Starting with a stock plant space in May of 800 square feet this poinsettia crop requires 15,000 square

Fig. 7—7. Pot plants must be moved to different areas periodically, and carts that can be used for this purpose save time and labor.

Fig. 7—8. A bicycle wheel cart such as this moves pot plants readily, and it can be maneuvered in narrow walks.

feet finishing in December. There is no possible way to have the available space occupied with young plants and then still have room for these plants when they mature. Some of the increase in space for poinsettias required in August is for propagation space, and some of the decreased space requirement in September indicates that the stock plants were discarded.

Fig. 7—9. In greenhouses where there is a lot of movement of pot plants a trolley conveyor can be a big time saver.

Azaleas really do not increase in size during forcing, thus they are placed at the finish spacing when they are first brought in. It must be kept in mind, however, that the azaleas do require cool storage facilities, such as cold frames or refrigerators, in addition to the greenhouse forcing space. The young plants also would need some greenhouse space in late spring when they are received, and azaleas require an outdoor growing area during the summer.

Lilies are started pot to pot and then spaced out gradually to the finish spacing of about 1 square foot per pot. Lilies develop faster at high temperatures, and they are shifted from one temperature house to another in the attempt to have them at just the right stage of development for Easter. Lilies rotate very well with poinsettias as they are started just after the poinsettias clear the benches.

The dormant hydrangeas are brought in for Easter forcing shortly after Christmas, and they can use space that was occupied by poinsettias. The dormant plants are started pot to pot and spaced as needed to about 2 square feet for each 3-cane plant at the finish. The Mother's Day hydrangea plants are started in late January. In addition to greenhouse forcing space, the dormant hydrangeas need either cold frame or refrigerated storage in the fall. Some space will be required in the spring for the young plants, and an outdoor growing area for the summer is needed for hydrangeas.

The pot plant grower is interested in keeping all of the available space occupied at all times of the year, and he can do this by fitting in other crops with the holiday pot plants. Any of the available space in January, February, and March commonly is used for forcing azaleas and potted bulbs such as tulips and hyacinths. Several different means are used for putting the space to work during the summer and early fall. An additional crop or two of pot mums may be grown for sale in the fall. Quite often the poinsettia propagation area is expanded, and rooted cuttings or 2¼ inch poinsettias are sold to other growers in late summer or early fall. Some of the area may be used for forcing off-season azaleas.

Other crops might be grown for the summer period only. Gloxinias can be a good three-month summer crop, and some growers produce a summer crop of foliage plants. Crops such as Christmas begonias or cyclamen can be grown during the summer and finished for late fall and Christmas, or they may be sold to other growers in early fall for finishing for Christmas. In some instances pot plant crops are rotated with cut flower crops, but this often requires considerable revision of the area between crops.

Most pot plants need to be staked and sleeved before being shipped. Either cane or wire stakes can be used for supporting pot plants. Even sturdy plants should be staked if they are going to be transported any appreciable distance.

Placing a paper sleeve around the pot plant protects it and speeds handling. Sleeving is rapid, too, as the sleeves are pulled up over the plant as it sits on a stand that holds the sleeves.

Fig. 7—10. Pot plants can be sleeved rapidly and it protects the plant in shipment.

Azalea

Azaleas are flowered from mid-December through May, although in some instances they are flowered the year around. Most of the plants are produced from rooted cuttings, but a few varieties are propagated by grafting. Propagation and the production of young plants take place in the South or on the East or West Coast where the plants can be grown continuously outdoors. The young plants are shipped to the greenhouse growers in the spring, they are grown outdoors during the summer, given cool storage in the fall, and forced into flower during the winter.

Azaleas, like most other pot plants, are priced and sold by the size pot the plant is in. During the growing period, however, the plants are sized by the diameter of the top of the plant. Varieties vary considerably in their growth, but the azalea grower buys about 3-inch to 5-inch plants in May or June and plans to finish the largest percentage of them in 6-inch azalea pots.

- **THE SMALL AZALEAS ARE STARTED IN
  THE GREENHOUSE IN LATE SPRING**

Most pot plant growers have their available greenhouse space occupied in the spring with plants being forced for Easter, Mother's Day, and Decoration Day. They may not have any room to start young azaleas until May. Azaleas are planted about 6 inches by 6 inches in peat in benches and grown at 60° night temperature. In some areas azaleas are grown in field soil, but coarse, poultry grade peat is recommended for growing azaleas in the greenhouse. As soon as root growth is observed, they should be given an application of nitrogen fertilizer with repeat applications every two weeks. In June the plants are potted and grown outdoors under lath or screen cloth, and they are pinched in June when the shoots are long enough to handle. If the plants are received early enough in the spring they are pinched in the greenhouse in May and pinched again outdoors in June.

Azaleas are not always potted for outdoor growing. Sometimes they are bedgrown and then dug and potted before being placed in cold frames in the fall. The main disadvantage in bedgrowing is that the plants make huge root systems, and much of the roots must be cut off before they can be potted in the fall.

It is a big advantage to have irrigation lines over the outdoor azalea beds so that the plants can be watered or misted easily. Azaleas need to be thoroughly watered, and periodic misting throughout the day will improve growth, too.

Fertilizer applications should be made every two weeks. An analysis of approximately 20-5-5 is good for azaleas. Be sure to water the plants just before making a fertilizer application. An occasional application of Sequestrene Fe 330 may be needed. It is used at the rate of ¼ pound per 100 gallons of water and drenched on the soil. Growth is best in somewhat acid conditions, but if plants are grown in

Fig. 7—11. Greenhouse production of growing-on azaleas in Alabama. (Blackwell Nurseries photograph)

Fig. 7—12. Azalea plant production under plastic screen in Florida.

Fig. 7—13. Growing-on azaleas produced in 3-inch peat pots. (Blackwell Nurseries photograph)

peat, and if acid-type fertilizers are used constantly, it may become too acid. Acidity readings should be made periodically, and iron sulfate may need to be added if the mixture is alkaline, or lime if the pH is below 5.

Before danger of frost in September the plants are moved to frames where they can be protected. The flower buds are very sensitive at this stage and can be frozen very easily by temperatures slightly below freezing for even a brief period. Keep the plants growing in the frames during this time by watering and fertilizing regularly.

- **AZALEAS NEED A COOL STORAGE PERIOD OF 50° OR LESS FOR AT LEAST FOUR WEEKS TO MATURE THE FLOWER BUDS**

Cool storage can be provided in cold frames or cool greenhouses if the temperatures can be regulated satisfactorily. For azaleas that are going to be forced for Christmas, the cool period must start the first of October. In many areas, cooling at this time requires a refrigerated storage. Regardless of where the cooling is done, the temperature needs to be uniformly below 50°, and the plants must be kept watered but not wet. If the plants are stored in a dark location, many leaves may drop. Leaf drop can be prevented by lighting the plants with 100 watt lamps, 4 feet apart and 2 feet above the plants for twelve hours a day.

- **FORCING AZALEAS IN SEASON**

Plants to be flowered for Christmas are taken out of cool storage and placed in 60° greenhouses about November 1. Some varieties require more cool storage than others, and only the varieties that need a short, cool storage period can be forced satisfactorily for Christmas. Some varieties require as much as eight weeks of cool storage, and because of this they cannot be forced until later in the season. During forcing, syringe the plants periodically, and keep them well watered after good root growth starts. The plants should be fertilized once or twice during the forcing period. If new shoot growth develops just below the flower buds, it should be removed by breaking out to the side.

During the natural azalea season the first plants are forced for Christmas, and many azaleas are forced for Valentine's Day and Easter. Because of warm temperatures in the spring it is difficult to hold azaleas for Mother's Day. It is not possible to flower azaleas consistently for Mother's Day unless refrigerated storage is available.

● FORCING AZALEAS THE YEAR AROUND

It is possible to flower some azalea varieties at any time of the year if the right conditions are provided. Leafy, vegetative growth of azaleas is promoted in long days at warm temperatures of 60° or higher. The plants are grown in these conditions until they are salable size. They are then placed in conditions that are best for formation and development of flower buds. Azalea flower buds form most readily at 60° or higher in reduced light or short days. Growth regulator chemicals can be used to promote flower bud formation on some varieties of azaleas. These chemicals cause the leafy, vegetative growth to terminate, and flower buds are then formed. Very often more than one flower bud forms on each stem, producing a cluster of flowers at the stem tips.

B-Nine is used at .15% (4 ounces per gallon of solution) for two applications a week apart or at .25% (6 ounces per gallon of solution) for one application. Cycocel is used at .3% (3 ounces per gallon of water) for two applications a week apart. Either chemical can be used successfully if the plants are in otherwise suitable conditions. The plants are sprayed to run-off. All azaleas do not react in the same way to these chemicals. Trials should be made before they are used on a large scale. Cycocel and B-Nine are not used in combination. Either one material or the other can be used. About two months after treatment the flower buds should be developed sufficiently so that the plants can be placed in cool storage for maturing the flower buds.

The azaleas need at least four weeks of 50° or cooler storage before they can be forced. The plants should be kept moist in storage, but not over-watered. Leaf drop will be minimized if the plants are lighted for twelve hours each day.

● **THERE ARE SEVERAL TYPES OF AZALEAS**

Azaleas really should be called rhododendrons, but they have been referred to for so long in the greenhouse business as azaleas that there would be confusion if they are called by another name. The large flowered types are indica or Belgium azaleas and the small flowered types are kurumes. The rutherfordiana azaleas have medium-sized flowers. Many of the indicas must be propagated by grafting, which makes them a more expensive plant and limits their use. The rutherfordiana azaleas have increased in popularity as they produce many good size flowers and are grown rather easily.

Most of the varieties grown in the greenhouse cannot be used as landscape azaleas because the flower buds do not stand cold temperatures. The florist azalea can be planted out successfully only in milder climates.

● **SOME AZALEA TROUBLES**

Chlorotic or yellow leaves indicate a deficiency of iron in the plant. This deficiency may be caused by a lack of iron in the soil or it may be due to a lack of roots. If the root growth is poor, new roots will have to be developed before an application of iron will do any good. Be sure that the water drainage is good, and that the fertilizer level is not too high. For an iron fertilizer use Sequestrene 330 Fe at the rate of ¼ pound per 100 gallons of water.

The growth of new shoots at the base of the flower buds during the forcing period is an irritation as they must be removed or the flower may not open. This happens more with some varieties than with others. Actually it indicates that the earlier flower forming conditions were not as good as they could have been. In ideal conditions these shoots would have been flower buds, forming multiple or cluster buds on each stem. For better flower bud promotion be sure that the night temperature is maintained above 60°, that the plants are in short days or partially shaded, and that one of the growth regulant chemicals is used.

Azaleas are infested easily with nematodes. Since most of the young plants are grown in warm climates where nematodes commonly are present in the field soils, careful control measures need to be taken to produce nematode-free plants.

Phytophthora is a common root disease of azaleas. Dexon 35 used at the rate of 4 ounces per 100 gallons of water and drenched on the soil once a month should give control.

Leaf drop is associated with plants that are kept too wet in storage or in too dark conditions. Keep the soil moist but not wet in storage, and light the plants with 100 watt lamps 4 feet apart and 2 feet above the plants.

Bedding Plants

Bedding plants are produced for spring sales. Most of them are annual plants that are grown from seed, and the customer plants them in his garden yearly. Usually some vegetable plants are produced along with the flower plants. Bedding plants are around a 3-month to 5-month crop depending on how they are handled. The seed is sown in January, February, or March, the seedlings are pricked-off to pots or

Fig. 7—14. Seed of F-1 hybrid petunias being produced in California under rigidly controlled conditions. All plants shown are females—they have had their own pollen removed (emasculation) before pollination with the pollen from a selected parent line. (Bodger Seeds, Ltd., photograph)

Fig. 7—15. Parent line petunias used in the production of F-1 hybrid seed in California. (Bodger Seeds, Ltd., photograph)

containers, and the plants are ready for sale in May. The market for bedding plants varies considerably in different areas. In the South the demand is very heavy for Mother's Day. In the North sales are best around Decoration Day. There is a demand for larger plants in flower as well as smaller plants not in flower.

• STRUCTURES FOR GROWING BEDDING PLANTS

No special type structures are required for growing bedding plants, but it happens that the bedding plants are produced in the spring of the year when much of the greenhouse space is occupied with spring holiday crops and regular greenhouse space is not available until late in the season. In order to get the space that is needed for bedding plants from January to June, very often temporary structures of some kind have to be used. Since these structures are used for only a portion of the year, the cost of the structure should be as low as possible.

Good greenhouse space is needed for the germination of the seed since accurate control of temperature and light is necessary. There are a lot of plants per seed flat, however, and they do not require much space. Since the seedlings should be pricked-off as soon as they can be handled, the seed flats will be in the greenhouse only a few weeks. The seedlings are transplanted in different ways, but regardless of the method used the transplanted seedlings will require about thirty-five times more space than the seed flat from which they came. This is a big increase in size of area, and depending on the size plants that are going to be finished, the space may be needed for only two to three months in the spring. Either cold frames or low-cost plastic houses are used commonly for bedding plant production in the spring.

Of the two structures the plastic houses are probably the best. They may cost more to construct than cold frames, but a better job of growing can be done in them. It is difficult to control temperatures and ventilation in cold frames, and they are back-breakers in which to work. If a heating system and an exhaust fan can be added to the plastic house, there will be much better control over the growth of the crop.

- ● THE SEED FLATS MUST BE KEPT WARM AND MOIST

Wooden flats are used for sowing seed. They are about 15 inches by 20 inches by 2¾ inches in size. There must be cracks between the bottom boards so that water will drain out readily. The flat is filled with the finely screened soil mixture, the soil is firmed, and the surface of the soil is leveled. The soil for the seed flat must be fine enough so that it makes good contact with the finest seed, but still it must drain well. Usually a mixture of shredded soil and peat moss is satisfactory. Superphosphate and calcium fertilizers may be added to the soil mixture, but the other fertilizers must be at low levels. Be sure that the soil mixture, flats, and area where the flats are to be set are carefully steam sterilized.

It is best to sow seed in rows, and fine seed such as petunia should be sown on the surface. Coarse seed such as marigold can be covered with a light layer of the soil mixture after sowing. If a mist system is used for the seed propagation area, the flats can be watered by using the mist system. If the flats are watered by hand, a fog nozzle should be used for the initial watering so that the seed is not disturbed or washed away. If a mist system is not used, the seed flats will need to

Fig. 7—16. A seed flat with bedding plant seedlings. Note that the seed flat was filled almost to the top with fine soil and that the seed was sown in rows. This allows for better air movement around the seedlings and less chance of disease.

be covered so that the surface of the soil stays uniformly moist at all times.

The seed should be germinated at 70°, and most varieties will be up in one to two weeks; however, ageratum and salvia are slower. As soon as the seed is germinated it should be placed in 60° temperature in full sunlight, given as much ventilation as possible, and the watering reduced to the minimum. Since the seedlings are now in cooler temperature they will not dry as rapidly, and the method of watering should be changed so that instead of keeping the surface of the soil constantly wet with light mistings, thorough waterings are given periodically with the surface drying somewhat between waterings.

- **THE SEEDLINGS SHOULD BE PRICKED-OFF AS SOON AS THEY CAN BE HANDLED**

This is when the first true leaves are unfolded. Most seedlings can be handled by the leaves.

Fig. 7—17. Bedding plants being grown in the greenhouse for sale in the spring.

Fig. 7—18. Petunias grown in 3-inch square peat pots for spring sales.

Fig. 7—19. Tomato seedlings grown in a flat for spring sales.

With a label or small trowel one "scoop" of plants is dug from the seed flat and placed on the potting bench. One seedling at a time is picked up by the leaves, the roots placed in the hole dibbled in the soil of the container, and the soil is firmed gently around the roots with one motion with thumbs and forefingers of both hands. The same soil mixture can be used for the containers as was used for the seed flats.

Various containers are used for bedding plants. There is an advantage in using containers that hold a dozen plants. This is a good sales-size unit, and it simplifies the problem of handling plants at the busy spring planting time. The containers are variously sized but a common size is 5½ inches by 7½ inches for a dozen plants, and they may be made from either molded wood fiber or from molded plastic. The containers are handled in wooden flats, and the size container is used that fits in the flats. In some instances the seedlings are pricked-off to flats and spaced about 2 inches by 2 inches—100 plants to the flat. This has fallen in disfavor somewhat because of the necessity for digging the plants by the dozen when they are sold.

Bedding plants are grown in various sizes depending on the customs of the particular market area. In some areas the customers demand that the plants be in flower, and in other areas most of the plants are sold in the smaller stage before they are in flower. Plants to be sold in flower must be grown in larger size containers than those that are going to be sold as small plants. Actually the small plants transplant to the garden better than the bigger plants do, and if the customers would accept the plants before they are in flower, it would be an advantage to them.

The bedding plants usually are grown at 50°, and they must be watered and fertilized regularly. Fertilizer should be applied in the liquid form because a much more uniform application can be made this way, and it is also easier. Applying some fertilizer with each watering by means of a fertilizer injector is fine. If this cannot be done, an application of 25-5-20 or equivalent should be made every two weeks at the rate of 3 pounds per 100 gallons of water. Bedding plants should be grown in full sunlight.

• SOW THE SEED AT THE RIGHT TIME FOR THE SIZE PLANT WANTED

Petunias to be flowered in 3-inch pots for Decoration Day are sowed January 1 and then pricked-off to flats or small pots before being shifted to 3-inch pots. Petunias and most of the other plants are sowed about March 1 when they are going to be finished as small plants in flats or containers for Decoration Day. Marigolds are sown at least two weeks later.

Pansies are handled quite differently. The seed is sowed in July and August and the young plants are planted out in frames in early fall. After frost they are either mulched or covered with sash. They are uncovered in early spring and started in growth, and the plants are dug and sold in flower in May.

Cabbage is sowed in February and March as it is planted outdoors as soon as the garden can be worked.

For small plant sales, tomatoes are sown about six weeks before they are to be sold. In some areas there is a good market for tomatoes in 3-inch pots. These may be started two to three months before they will be sold.

Peppers are grown at higher temperatures, and they must be started at least eight weeks before they are to be sold. Peppers should be grown at 60° temperature.

● BEDDING PLANT TROUBLES

Aphids and slugs are the most common pests on bedding plants. Meta Systox-R controls aphids and Slugit, a liquid metaldehyde preparation, or Zectran can be used for slugs.

Damping-off can occur in the seed flats or after the plants are pricked-off. Careful sterilization of soil and equipment is very important, and the plants should be given as much air circulation as possible. If an infestation does occur, soil drenches with either Morsodren or Dexon 35 and Terraclor 75 should give control.

Fig. 7—20. The growth regulant chemical, B-Nine, can be used to reduce the height of some bedding plants. (Naugatuck Chemical photograph)

Chrysanthemum

Until it was learned how to regulate the time of the flowering of chrysanthemums, pot mums were flowered only during the natural season in the fall. Typically one rooted cutting was planted in a 6-inch pot early in the summer and pinched several times to produce a bushy plant by fall. By providing long days and short days as needed the pot mum now is flowered the year around in great quantities. Five rooted cuttings are planted in a 6-inch azalea pot (¾ pot), grown briefly in long days, pinched, and then given short days until they flower. This makes pot mums about a three-month crop.

- **CHRYSANTHEMUMS ARE PROPAGATED BY ROOTED STEM TIP CUTTINGS**

Stem tip cuttings are used, and they root readily in two to four weeks depending on the variety. The difficult part of mum propagation is having good quality, disease free cuttings in the quantities that are needed at the right time. It really is a job for the specialist, and for that reason the rooted cuttings are purchased from the specialist propagator.

- **IF A SINGLE PART OF POT MUM GROWING PROCEDURE COULD BE NAMED AS BEING THE MOST IMPORTANT, IT WOULD HAVE TO BE THE SOIL MIXTURE**

The soil mixture must be coarse. Mum roots just don't grow well in a closely-packed, heavy soil, and good top growth then is not possible. New root growth should be visible about three days after planting. The fertilizer program should be started with the next watering as a continuous supply of nitrogen is very essential for good growth of the young plant. If the soil mixture is sufficiently coarse and porous, the pot mum will need to be watered often but the root growth will be rapid as the air supply will be excellent in the porous soil mixture. The small, plastic tube systems of watering pot plants can do a fine job with pot mums, and labor is conserved. Supplying fertilizer with each watering by means of a fertilizer injector is the best way to make sure that some fertilizer is always available. If phosphorus and calcium fertilizer are added to the potting soil, a good fertilizer formula for injection feeding is 25-0-25 or 25-5-20. Most

Fig. 7—21. Pot mums are grown in the open or under plastic screen in Florida. (Floral Acres, Inc., photograph)

fertilizers applied in the liquid form have no calcium in them. Don't overlook the addition of calcium fertilizer to the soil before potting.

Some varieties of pot mums are well known for poor root growth when conditions are less than ideal. It is particularly important that coarse, porous soil be used for these varieties. Wilting of the leaves during hot weather does not always indicate that the soil is dry. It can indicate that the soil drains slowly, because the root growth is slow in poorly aerated soil. Applying more water to such a soil only aggravates the situation. It may help to knock the plant out of the pot and then set it back in lightly; a little gravel can be placed in the bottom of the pot before the plant is set back in it. Of course the soil mixture should be corrected before the next plants are potted.

The rooted cuttings should be planted as shallow as possible and spaced equally around the edge of the pot. Planting the cuttings at an angle over the edge of the pot gives the cuttings more room to grow, and this procedure makes a bushier plant. Pot mums are lighted for a week or more after they are planted.

Growth of the young plants will be faster and of better quality if a mist system is provided for the plants during this period. They should be misted just often enough so that the leaves remain moist. In order to conserve power the plants are often placed pot to pot in the lighted area and then gradually spaced out in other areas to a final spacing of 1½ square feet per pot.

● POT MUMS ARE A 60° CROP

Chrysanthemums need to be furnished 60° night temperatures with 5° to 10° warmer during the day, and some varieties flower more uniformly with 65° night temperatures.

During the summer the high temperatures may cause delay in flowering and the fading of some colors. The delay in flowering can be very important as in some hot spells it has delayed crops two to three weeks, and in addition, the stems stretch during this period, making an undesirable looking plant. Air cooling and air circulation for pot mums during the summer are a definite help.

The day length is naturally long enough for mums from late May until the last of July; however, during the rest of the year the plants must be lighted when they need long days. The lighting can be done with 60 watt lamps placed 2 feet above the plants and 4 feet apart. Turn on the lights as closely to midnight as possible, and use the lights each night. Light two hours per night in August and May; three hours in September-October and March-April; and four hours November through February. Somebody needs to check regularly to be sure that the lights are working properly. Any failure can cause malformed flowering.

The days are naturally short from September to the middle of March. Black cloth is placed over the plants for short days during the rest of the year. The cloth should be drawn at 7 P.M. and removed at 7 A.M. If it is drawn earlier during the hot weather in the summer, the temperatures are very warm under the cloth, and this causes delay in flowering. Temperatures under the cloth can be reduced somewhat by lifting the sides after dark, and then dropping them

Fig. 7—22. The plant on the left was treated with the growth regulant chemical, B-Nine, and the plant on the right was not. By use of such chemicals the height of pot mums can be regulated as desired. (Naugatuck Chemical photograph)

again before light in the morning. The use of air circulation fans during the summer helps, too.

• THE HEIGHT OF POT MUMS CAN BE REGULATED

Chrysanthemum varieties for pots are chosen not only on the color, size, and shape of the flower but also on the shape and height plant that it makes. If the variety has good qualities, but there are some height problems, this can be adjusted by using the right growing schedule. The varieties are classified by the propagators as short, medium, or tall growers, and schedules are provided for each group. The short growing varieties are given the longest period of long days, and they are given some long days after the pinch. This gives them longer stems before the flowers are formed. The tall growing varieties are given a minimum period of long days, and very often the pinch is

Fig. 7—23. The plant on the right was treated with Phosfon and the plant on the left was not treated. The amount and time of treatment can be adjusted so that the desired height pot mum is produced with the chemical height retardant, Phosfon. (U. S. D. A. photograph)

made after the start of short days. The medium varieties are grown in long days for a short period of time and then pinched, and short days are started at the same time.

In spite of starting short days immediately and using the delayed pinch after the start of the short days, some varieties are still too tall for use as pot mums. Some chemicals can be used to regulate the growth on such varieties. If a .25% solution of B-Nine is sprayed on such varieties about two weeks after the plants are pinched, the plants will be more compact, the stems will be heavier, and the foliage a darker green. Phosfon can be used also to regulate the growth of pot mums; however, it must be applied to the soil. Phosfon dust can be mixed with the soil before the plants are potted, or Phosfon liquid can be drenched on the soil when the shoots start to break after the pinch. Phosfon will have an effect on the growth of the plants even if the clay pot is dipped in a Phosfon solution before potting. Phosfon persists in the soil, and care must be taken that the treated soil is not re-used on other plants that are short enough.

When used properly these chemicals are excellent tools for regulating the height of pot mums. Trials must be made by each grower before he uses them, as the effect of the chemical varies with the variety that it is used on, the soil and watering methods, the fertilizer program, and the time of the year when it is used. Generally height control is needed on some varieties of pot mums during the summer, but none at all may be needed during the winter.

- **THE PLANTS MUST GROW LONG ENOUGH BEFORE THE PINCH IS MADE SO THAT IT CAN BE MADE IN THE NEW GROWTH**

This is a soft pinch, and just the tip of the plant is removed. This produces the greatest number of uniform, heavy shoots following the pinch. A minimum of three good shoots per plant is needed as the finished plant should have fifteen flowers or more.

Most pot mums are grown with the side flower buds removed so there is just a single, terminal flower per stem. This disbudding is a continual task that must be done as soon as the buds can be handled. The small buds easily are rolled out to the side. In some areas pot mums are grown without disbudding the stems. Each stem then has a spray of flowers.

Some large flowered varieties are grown as single-stem pot mums without pinching. These are called single-stem pot mums, and seven plants are used in a 6-inch pot. This provides a different quality pot mum, which in some areas is popular particularly in larger sized pots for the holidays.

- **THE FLOWERS SHOULD BE WELL DEVELOPED BEFORE POT MUMS ARE SOLD**

The pot mum keeps best in the hands of the consumer if it is allowed to remain in the greenhouse until the flower is almost fully expanded. Some customers feel that if they buy a pot chrysanthemum when the flower is just starting to open it will last that much longer for them in the home, but this is not true. However, some customers will not allow themselves to believe this, and it is best to plan on having holiday plants at several stages of maturity to satisfy all of the customers. It is better to make two or three plantings at weekly intervals for each holiday; thus the flowers will be at all stages of development from partially to wide open.

- **THE MOST POPULAR POT MUM VARIETIES ARE INCURVES OR LARGE DECORATIVES**

The variety Bonnaffon DeLuxe was used as the standard pot mum variety for a number of years, and then it was replaced gradually as newer varieties were introduced. On most markets yellow varieties are desired in greatest quantity. Some spiders, anemones, and feathered decoratives are grown in small quantities for novelty items.

- **GARDEN MUM VARIETIES CAN BE SOLD AS SPRING POTS**

Many mothers would like to be able to plant the mums they receive for Mother's Day outdoors so that they will flower again. If garden variety chrysanthemums are used for some of the Mother's Day pot mums, these can be planted outdoors after they have been enjoyed indoors, and they will flower again in the fall. It is best to send printed instructions along with these plants so mother will know just what to do with it. The individual plants in the pot should be separated, planted in the garden, and cut back, leaving 2- to 4-inch stems on the plants. When the new shoots are about 3 inches long, the tips should be pinched off. The plant should be watered regularly, fertilized once a month, and the shoots pinched until the first week in August. Each plant then will be a small bush, and will flower in late October before the hard freeze.

For flowering for Mother's Day the garden varieties do not need to be lighted or shaded. The day length is about right for them at that time of the year. They are potted about March 1 and pinched a week later. The garden varieties then flower the first week in May in natural conditions.

As many of the garden varieties have rather small flowers, they are grown very often without disbudding. Each stem then has a spray of flowers.

● **APHIDS ARE THE MOST PERSISTENT PEST OF POT MUMS**

Aphids feed mainly on the upper portions of chrysanthemum stems. They are easy to detect, but they do crawl under the bud scales and escape detection as well as insecticides at times. They should be completely controlled before flowering time as it is almost impossible to do a good job of killing them after the flowers are open.

Two spotted mites are pests of pot mums, and they commonly inhabit the under side of the lower leaves. They can be controlled on chrysanthemums with several different materials, and there is no excuse for having an infestation. Be sure that the plants are clean before time for flowering, as they are much more difficult to control after the flowers are open.

There are several diseases of chrysanthemums. Because the chrysanthemum propagator has devised means of producing disease-free stock these diseases can be kept in control if the pot mum grower does a careful job of steam sterilizing potting soil and handling equipment.

Foliage Plants

As the name implies these are not sold as flowering plants. They are plants that are known primarily for the pleasing effect of their leaves rather than the effect of the flower. They are plants that can survive in poorly lighted and dry conditions such as those found in

Fig. 7-24. Philodendron pertusum stock being grown in a plastic screen house in Florida. During the winter houses such as this are covered with polyethylene film and heated. (Evergreen Gardens of Apopka, Inc., photograph)

Fig. 7—25. Sansevieria laurenti grown in a slat shed in central Florida. In southern Florida sansevieria is grown in the open. (Evergreen Gardens of Apopka, Inc., photograph)

Fig. 7—26. Sansevieria growing in open fields in southern Florida. Note the irrigation lines spaced regularly through the field.

Fig. 7—27. Nephthytis Green Gold stock is grown in plastic screen houses or in slat sheds in central Florida, but it is propagated and grown in heavily shaded greenhouses. This is the standard method of operation for most foliage plants produced in central Florida. In south Florida or in Puerto Rico the entire production may be in slat sheds or plastic screen houses. (Evergreen Gardens of Apopka, Inc., photograph)

homes and offices. Foliage plants are very often used for long term decorations rather than a momentary or holiday display.

The young plants are grown in warm climates such as Florida, Puerto Rico, and California, and they are shipped to the greenhouse grower for growing-on. Most of these plants grow best at temperatures of 70° and above, and even in the warmer climates this requires some protection during certain periods of the year. In Florida the stock plants are grown in slat sheds that can be covered with film plastic during the winter and heated. Most of the propagation is done in greenhouses in Florida. In Puerto Rico the winter temperatures are higher, and slat sheds only are used for growing stock and for propagation. Some stock is grown outdoors in California, but propagation and much of the growing are in greenhouses.

• FOLIAGE PLANTS GROW WITH HEAT AND HUMIDITY

The requirements of foliage plants vary somewhat, but generally they grow best in less light, and at higher temperatures, and in more moist conditions than other greenhouse crops. Only about 1,000 foot candles of light are needed. Foliage plants should be partially shaded throughout the year. Usually the glass will need to be shaded, and a cloth shade is drawn above the plants. A minimum night temperature of 70° is used, with day temperatures of 75° to 80°. One of the most common problems with foliage plants is too cool temperatures in the greenhouse. They are high temperature plants and just don't grow at temperatures below 70°. The humidity needs to be kept high by constant misting. Most of the foliage plants grow best in soils that contain much organic matter; peat moss is used most commonly.

When foliage plants are taken into the home, office, or public building they are in a much different environment than they were in at the greenhouse. The light intensity may be 100 foot candles or less, which is only about one tenth the amount that the plants received in the greenhouse, and the air in most buildings is very dry. Some locations in buildings are too hot and others are too cold. With such unfavorable surroundings foliage plants do not really grow much. They may be able to maintain themselves, and that is about all. Actually a lot of growth is not required or wanted in most situations as

Fig. 7—28. Flatting ivy cuttings for rooting and growing on in California. (Los Angeles Plant Co., photograph)

Fig. 7—29. Euonymus stock plants grown outdoors in California. (Los Angeles plant Co. photograph)

Fig. 7—30. Boxwood being grown in flats outdoors in California except for temporary frost protection. (Los Angeles Plant Co. photograph)

Fig. 7—31. Euonymus Silver Queen grown under lath in California. (Los Angeles plant Co. photograph)

Fig. 7—32. Foliage plants growing in a northern greenhouse.

the plants would outgrow their location. Since the growth is so slow with foliage plants in the home and office, they use very little water and fertilizer. Customers should be warned to use both water and fertilizer sparingly on their foliage plants.

• A GREAT NUMBER OF PLANTS ARE GROWN AS FOLIAGE PLANTS

Aglaonema is propagated in Florida and Puerto Rico as rooted cuttings and seedlings. *A. simplex* (Chinese Evergreen) and *A. commutatum* (Variegated Chinese Evergreen) are used most commonly of the aglaonemas. In smaller sizes they may be used in dish gardens and in larger sizes as specimen plants.

Aralias are used primarily as dish garden plants, but in some instances they are used as large specimen plants. The primary area of propagation is Puerto Rico for *A. balfouriana (Polyscias balfouriana)* as rooted cuttings, Florida for *A. elegantissima (Dizygotheca elegan-*

tissima) as seedlings, and California for *A. seiboldi (Fatsia Japonica)* as rooted cuttings.

The cactus comes from California. It is propagated from seed and in some instances from cuttings. Some large specimen plants are used, but the primary use is in dish gardens.

The small leaf crotons (codiaeum) are propagated as rooted cuttings in Florida and California, and the larger leaf crotons are propagated as rooted cuttings or moss-rooted layers in Florida. These are some of the more colorful foliage plants. The small leaf varieties are used in gardens and the large leaf varieties as specimen plants.

Dieffenbachias are used primarily as specimen plants, although small plants are sometimes used in dish gardens. The use of rooted cuttings from cane is the most common means of propagation. Cane may be shipped in direct from Puerto Rico, or small potted plants that have been grown from cane may be obtained in Florida. Serious disease problems limit the use of the dieffenbachias.

The dracaenas are used considerably as foliage plants. *D. godseffiana* and *D. sanderiana* are mainly dish garden plants; and *D. marginata, D. massangeana,* and *D. warnecki* are specimen plants. The dracaenas are propagated as stem tip or cane rooted cuttings primarily in Puerto Rico.

The types of ficus (Rubber Plants) that are used most commonly make large specimen plants. They are propagated as moss-rooted layers in Florida and Puerto Rico.

The ivies are propagated in northern greenhouses or in California. They are used in dish garden work. Many varieties of English Ivy are used and some of the cissus such as Grape Ivy.

Nephthytis is propagated as rooted cuttings from cane in Florida. Small plants are used in dish gardens, and the larger plants as totem poles.

The Neanthe Bella palm is used very often as a dish garden plant, but the bigger plants also make good specimen plants. Several other palm varieties are used as specimen plants. Palms are propagated from seed mainly in Florida.

The peperomias are dish garden plants. They are propagated as rooted cuttings in northern greenhouses, and in some instances in Florida. Disease limits their use.

The philodendrons are the most popular of the foliage plants. *P. cordatum* is the small leafed variety that is used in dish gardens and as totem poles. It is propagated as cane or leaf cuttings. The large split leaf philodendron is *P. pertusum,* and it is propagated as rooted cuttings or as a modified moss-rooted layer. Other than *P. cordatum,* the philodendrons are used as large specimen plants or totem poles. Florida is the main source for philodendrons.

Sansevieria are used in dish gardens but also as specimen plants. They have an entirely different character from the other foliage plants and add interest in a planting. They are propagated as leaf cuttings or divisions in Florida.

There is a large group of plants known as succulents. A few of the more common ones are crassulas, echeverias, and sedums. These plants are used in dish gardens, and they are propagated by seed and cuttings in California.

• FOLIAGE PLANTS THAT ARE USED IN DISH GARDENS

The dish gardens are strictly an item for the home. Many of them are purchased directly for use in the home, and others are given as hospital or other gifts and then enjoyed in the home. The dish garden should contain plants that require similar conditions of light, temperature, and water.

In most instances it is best to ship in the rooted cuttings or the 2¼ inch plants from the specialist foliage producer in the South or West. The rooted cuttings are potted on arrival and used as needed. The plants that arrive in small pots can be used shortly after receipt. The dish garden should be something more than a collection of plants. Size, texture, and color of plants should be used to make a pleasing arrangement.

Low plants:

Aglaonema commutatum — variegated green and grey.

Aralia balfouriana — green leaves with white border.

Aralia elegantissima — interesting feathery texture.

Aralia seiboldi — star-shaped leaves.

Buxus japonica — Boxwood, bushy with small, shiny, green leaves.

Cactus — various shapes and sizes.

Croton Maculatum — green leaves splashed with yellow.

Croton Punctatum — narrow green and yellow variegated leaves.

Euonymus — white or yellow variegated leaves.

Fittonia argyroneura — green leaves, uniformly netted in white.

Hoya carnosa var. — waxy, green leaf with white border.

English Ivy — many interesting shapes and colors.

Maranta kerchoveana — Prayer Plant, dark green blotches on leaves.

Nephthytis — arrow-shaped leaves, green or variegated

Peperomia — several different leaf sizes, textures, and colors.

Philodendron cordatum — should be the backbone of most gardens.

Pilea cadierei — Aluminum Plant, green and silver leaf.

Pittosporum tobira — long, shiny, green leaves.

Pothos — good variegation, green with yellow or white.

Sansevieria hahni — variegated rosette.

Succulents —

   Aloe — rosettes of fleshy leaves, some variegated.

   Crassula arborescens — Jade Plant, fat green leaves edged red.

   Echeveria — rosettes of fleshy leaves, various colors.

   Haworthia — Crown of Pearls, rosette of sharply pointed leaves, dotted.

   Kalanchoe tomentosa — Panda Bear, white velvet leaves edged in brown.

Larger or upright plants:

   Aglaonema simplex — Chinese Evergreen, dark green, horizontal leaves.

   Dieffenbachia exotica — showy, variegated leaf.

   Dracaena godseffiana — large, colorful leaves in tiers; lots of character.

   Dracaena sanderiana — Striped Corn Plant, yellow and green variegation.

   Neanthe Bella palm — palms add the tropical touch.

   Philodendron florida — green leaf with red petiole.

Philodendron panduraeforme — long, green leaf.

Podocarpus macrophyllus—narrow, dark green leaves.

Sansevieria — upright, pointed leaves, green or with yellow edge.

Schefflera actinophylla—bright green, shiny leaf.

• FOLIAGE PLANTS FOR USE AS SPECIMEN PLANTS

These are larger foliage plants that are used in the home, office, restaurant, or other public building as a part of the interior decoration. Most of the specimen plants are shipped in from southern or western specialists as small plants and grown-on in the greenhouse to the desired size. Some of the slower growing plants are shipped in from the specialists in the large, finished size.

Aglaonema — several types used; *A. simplex* has dark green, rather horizontal leaves; *A. pseudo-brachteatum* and *A. treubi* have long, variegated leaves.

Aralia elegantissima (*Dizygotheca elegantissima*) — has long narrow leaves which give a light, feathery appearance.

Araucaria excelsa — Norfolk Island Pine; gives the appearance of a formal evergreen tree; branches are in tiers.

Bromeliads — many of these sold in flower or fruit.
Aechmea fasciata — pink and blue flowers.
Ananas comosus (Pineapple) — sold in fruit.
Neoregelia — used for foliage effect, spectabilis, Fingernail Plant, for red tip on leaves.
Vriesia splendens—Flaming Sword, has flaming red flower spike.

Citrus mitus—Calamondin Orange, sold in fruit.

Croton hybrids—very colorful variegated foliage.

Dieffenbachia—*D. amoena* has large, dark green leaves marked regularly with white; it is one of the larger dieffenbachias. *D. exotica* has lighter green leaves splashed with white.

Dracaena marginata—shiny, narrow dark-green leaves edged in red. Older plants lose bottom leaves, leaving interesting, crooked stems topped with tufts of leaves.

Dracaena   massangeana—Usually   older   canes   are   rooted   in
1- to 4-foot lengths. This gives the unusual effect of
a straight, heavy, tan cane with a tuft or two of
broad green and yellow striped leaves toward the
top.

Dracaena warnecki—an upright growing plant with long, narrow leaves with fine white stripes on green.

Ferns — mostly Boston Fern varieties.

Ficus decora — Rubber Plant, upright plant with large leaves.

Palms — Neanthe Bella or Kentia are used most commonly
although some other kinds are available.

Philodendron — the most popular large leafed foliage plant
is *P. pertusum*, Split Leaf Philodendron. Others are
P. emerald queen or *P. hastatum* with green arrow-
shaped leaves, *P. florida* with dark green, highly in-
dented leaves with red petioles, *P. panduraeforme*
with green fiddle-shaped leaves.

Schefflera actinophylla — glossy, bright green leaves.

• TOTEM POLE PLANTS

Several of the foliage plants vine or run if they are grown for
awhile. If they are trained up a pole or a slab of wood they are
referred to as totem poles. *Philodendron cordatum* or *Pothos wilcoxi*
are grown on 24-inch, 36-inch and 48-inch poles, and the larger leafed
philodendrons are grown from 24 inches to 72 inches although the 36-
inch and 48-inch sizes are the most popular.

Philodendron pertusum, Split Leaf Philodendron, is the large leaf
variety that is used the most for totem poles. Other varieties used are
P. panduraeforme, P. florida, P. emerald queen, P. hastatum, and *P.
dubium.* Combinations of these plants may be used in some instances,
and sometimes *Philodendron cordatum, Pothos wilcoxi,* or Nephthytis
Green Gold may be used together with one of the large leafed
philodendrons.

An interesting totem pole can be made using *Dracaena massangeana* as the pole and either *Philodendron cordatum* or Nephthytis
Green Gold for filler at the base.

Geranium

Geraniums are a spring crop, mainly for Decoration Day sales. Most of them are produced in 4-inch pots. If good growing conditions are furnished, it is possible to produce good 4-inch geraniums for Decoration Day from cuttings potted in January. In order to have a supply of cuttings at that time, either they are purchased from outdoor California operations, or the grower has stock plants in his own greenhouses for the production of cuttings.

• GERANIUM CUTTINGS FROM CALIFORNIA

The southern California climate is good for growing geraniums, and if the plants are kept disease free good cuttings can be produced reasonably there. Typically, the entire operation is outdoors and subject to extremes in weather. Occasional frosts, heavy rains, or unseasonably high temperatures can limit quality and production, but generally California geranium cutting production is reliable.

California geranium cuttings are shipped as unrooted, callused, or rooted cuttings. The price of California rooted cuttings is about the same as rooted cutting prices in the Midwest. Callused cuttings are about 1½ cent less. Unrooted geranium cuttings are about half the price of rooted cuttings. Callused cuttings are probably the best type of California cuttings to use as they can be potted immediately, and they grow as rapidly as, or possibly even better than, the rooted cuttings.

Geraniums are notoriously poor shippers. All California geraniums are shipped by air freight, and this is fast enough service to most parts of the country so that the plants arrive in good condition. However, geraniums must be unpacked and planted as soon as possible after they are received. Delays in transit or in handling the geraniums after they arrive can result in a serious loss of lower foliage and the start of some diseases. Shipping the cuttings moist, or overheating in transit, further aggravates the situation.

Shipping problems with geraniums are not confined to California stock. Midwest geraniums must be handled just as rapidly, and this can be a problem even with rather short distances as delays enroute are common with surface transportation.

Fig. 7—33. Geranium stock fields in southern California (Grand View Geranium Gardens photograph)

Fig. 7—34. Geranium cuttings being rooted in a plastic house in southern California. (Grand View Geranium Gardens photograph)

• PRODUCING CUTTINGS IN THE GREENHOUSE

Various methods of handling stock plants in greenhouses are used; however, the best plan is to grow the plant as tall as possible on a stake, then harvest the entire plant for cuttings in December or January. The best plants should be selected in the spring for growing on as stock plants, or new cultured stock should be purchased. The plants are planted in sterilized soil and staked. Use a good coarse soil

Fig. 7—35. Geranium stock plant grown upright in the greenhouse for production of stem tip and leaf bud cuttings. Cutting production can be increased by this method if the leaf bud cuttings can be used as well as the stem tip cuttings. (Johnston the Florist photograph)

and add superphosphate and calcium fertilizers to the soil before planting. As the plant grows, the side shoots are pinched each week, and the terminal shoot is allowed to continue growing upward.

Growth of the side shoots is improved very much if the large leaves are thinned out as the plant grows. Apparently this better growth is due to the increase in light and air circulation around the base of the plant.

Fig. 7—36. A house of 4-inch geraniums produced for Decoration Day. (Johnston the Florist photograph)

If the soil is well prepared before planting, growth of the plants will be rapid and they will need to be well watered and fertilized. Water should be kept off the leaves and upper portions of geranium plants, and watering should be done in the morning so that the air does not remain humid for a long period of time. Small plastic tube watering systems are very good for watering geranium stock plants; but because they are in large containers, two or more tubes should be used per plant or larger tubes should be used. The plants should be fertilized regularly. Applying fertilizer with each watering by means of a fertilizer injector is good, and 25-5-20 analysis fertilizer or its equivalent should be used at about ½ pound per 100 gallons of water applied.

Several weeks before the cutting harvest is to start the top of the plant is pinched. Pinching of the terminal tip of the plant promotes growth of the side shoots. The schedule for pinching the terminal and taking the cuttings will need to be adjusted to the specific needs at each greenhouse, but in many instances it is best to make the terminal pinch in late November. Stem tip cuttings then are taken in mid-January from all portions of the plant. In early February another crop of stem cuttings is taken, together with leaf bud cuttings wherever they are available. In early March the last crop of leaf bud cuttings is taken, and the remains of the stock plant are discarded. Leaf bud cuttings should not be taken unless the eye has started to grow. Shoot growth then is much more uniform after the leaf bud is rooted.

Geranium leaf bud cuttings are made by cutting the stem into sections each of which has one leaf with some growth started at the leaf axil. These stem sections are from 1 to 2 inches long, and they can be placed in the propagation bench with the leaf and the bud at the base of the leaf above the propagation medium. Plants that are grown from geranium leaf bud cuttings are just as good as those made from stem tip cuttings, but they do require a little more growing time, or higher temperatures, to make the same size plant. It is possible to get about one hundred cuttings per stock plant using this method. This is high production per plant, and there is the added advantage of getting the cuttings over a short period of time. However, approximately half the cuttings will be stem tip cuttings and half will be leaf-bud cuttings.

If geranium stock plants are not grown upright for leaf bud and stem tip cuttings, they are started in the same manner, but the plant is pinched during the summer and stem tip cuttings are taken starting in the fall. Stock plants should be allowed to flower once to verify the variety, but after that flower buds should be removed as they form. Shattering flower petals are often the start of a Botrytis infestation on the leaves. The large lower leaves also should be removed to give better light and air circulation to the shoots. The cuttings that are rooted in the fall can be used for larger plants in the spring or they must be grown very slowly to be 4-inch plants for Decoration Day.

When propagation of stem tip cuttings stops in March there still is a large stock plant remaining with this method of handling. In most instances it probably would be best to discard these stock plants and start the next year's stock plants from new plants later in the spring. In many instances the stock plants are carried over year after year, they become over-grown, and disease in the stock is more likely.

Cutting production from this method of handling geranium stock plants is from thirty to forty cuttings per plant. These are all stem tip cuttings, but they are produced over a long period of time.

The least desirable method of handling geranium stock plants is outdoors. All of the cuttings must be taken on outdoor stock in September before the frosts arrive, and this is much too early to start geraniums for flowering in late spring. When outdoor stock is used, the plants are grown slowly by keeping them dry, cool, and poorly fertilized. It is a very long "growing" period, and the plants are not of as good quality as those grown actively in the spring.

● **GERANIUM PROPAGATION**

With 55° air temperature and 60° to 65° bench temperature geraniums root in three to four weeks. They callus in about two weeks, and some growers pot the callused cuttings as they find that these root readily after potting, and the growth is as good or possibly better than that which results from waiting until the cuttings are rooted.

Coarse sand, perlite, or mixtures of perlite and peat can be used for rooting geraniums. The bench must drain perfectly, and geranium cuttings should be watered-in well after sticking and then watered sparingly. Keep the cuttings out of the direct sun by cloth over the bench. Do not place paper or cloth directly on the cuttings.

Geraniums can be rooted satisfactorily directly in 2¼ inch peat pots or clay pots. A very porous soil must be used for propagation in the pot, and after the cuttings are watered-in well the waterings are spaced as much as possible. After they are rooted these plants will need to be watered and fertilized more often than usual because of the porous soil mixtures that they are in.

● **KEEP THE GERANIUM GROWING ACTIVELY**

Use a coarse, well drained soil for geraniums for good growth in the shortest time. Most soils should have straw, strawy manure, or coarse peat moss added to them so they will be porous. Incorporate superphosphate and calcium fertilizers in the potting soil. Keep the plants well watered, and fertilize regularly with a fertilizer analysis such as 25-5-20. Small, plastic tube systems for watering geraniums are excellent, and applying fertilizer with each watering by means of an injector assures a continuous supply of fertilizer.

Some of the geranium varieties branch well without pinching; other varieties will need to be pinched. A hard pinch can be made in early February, or a soft pinch the first part of March, for plants to flower in May. Any early flowers should be pinched.

Geraniums should be grown at 55° minimum night temperature with day temperatures 5° to 10° warmer, and with the maximum amount of ventilation. Air circulation fans will be beneficial.

The cuttings are potted to 2¼-inch pots and then they are shifted to 4-inch pots when they are well rooted. The shift to 4-inch pots needs to be made before the plants become pot-bound and hard in the 2¼-inch pots. The small pots are grown pot to pot, and the 4-inch pots may be, too, for a short while after potting; however, they should be spaced as soon as possible as this helps the plant to branch and it becomes more bushy. Well spaced plants also allow for better air movement through the plants, and it reduces the amount of disease.

● **RED GERANIUMS ARE IN THE GREATEST DEMAND**

Preferences as to colors and varieties vary over the country, but the red geraniums are used the most, followed by light pink. For varieties, Irene and its sports account for a considerable portion of the geranium production. They have large flowers, and they produce many flowers. Irene leaves are so large that they are somewhat objectionable because they occupy so much room. The flowers do shatter, and this is always a problem, but the Irenes produce so many flowers that the shattering can be overlooked to some extent.

● **GERANIUM TROUBLES**

There are several serious diseases of geraniums, and some of these can be transmitted with the cutting. Be sure that the cuttings come from a disease-free source. Plants that are infected with virus, bacterial leaf spot and stem rot, or Pythium cannot really be cured, and it is much the best plan to start with cuttings that are free of these diseases. Steam sterilize soil and all handling equipment to be used around geraniums, and handle water carefully. When disease does occur, have it identified by an expert as the methods of control vary with the disease.

Plants that are in constantly wet soil are more likely to contract Pythium, and too moist air is ideal for Botrytis and oedema. Space the plants well so that air movement is good around them, and provide good ventilation at all times. Oedema is not actually a disease. It is a condition of corky or warty spots that can develop rapidly on the under side of the leaf in a humid atmosphere. Good ventilation and air movement stop the progress of oedema at once.

Botrytis seems to appear from nowhere and without notice. Apparently the spores of Botrytis are always present in the greenhouse, and if the conditions are suitable it can start in growth immediately. The leaf symptom of Botrytis is brown, dead areas with some general yellowing of the leaf. Quite often the diseased area of the leaf was started by a floret shattering from the flower and falling on the leaf. Moisture collects under the floret and Botrytis starts. Botrytis may also start in the moist area caused by two leaves that are touching each other. Botrytis can cause rot on geranium stems, too. It is most likely to start on cuts or wounds on the stem. The best controls for Botrytis are to keep the flowers picked from the stock plants as old flowers are very susceptible to the disease; keep the upper portions of the geranium dry; provide good air circulation around geraniums, for which purpose air circulation fans can be a real help; space the plants well as this allows better air circulation; and do not cut or wound the stem of the cutting any more than necessary.

A few geranium propagators have facilities to provide geranium cuttings from culture-indexed stock. This means that the stock plants from which they take the cuttings have been tested in a laboratory for some disease organisms, and they have been found free of them. This is a valuable aid in the production of disease-free cuttings, but it must be realized that there are limitations also. Some propagators may be equipped to do a more thorough job than others, but it is quite likely with geraniums that the culture-indexing procedure is designed to determine the presence or absence of the organisms that cause bacterial stem rot and leaf spot, and Pythium. Viruses may or may not be present, but this particular culture-indexing would not determine that.

In some instances the procedures used also may culture and index the stock plants for virus diseases.

In spite of culture-indexing, cuttings from this stock can and will become infested with these diseases and other geranium diseases if they are subjected to the organisms. The cutting from culture-indexed stock will remain disease-free only if it is placed in disease-free surroundings. It is very important to steam sterilize the soil, pots, and handling equipment for geraniums, and all other precautions should be taken to assure that the plants are kept free from disease.

● **GERANIUMS CAN BE GROWN FROM SEED**

Geraniums are not commonly grown from seed because the seed of the most desirable varieties has not been available. When the seed is available for the type geraniums that are needed, there will be a big change in the production of geraniums. Apparently about the same length of time is required to produce a 4-inch geranium plant from seed as from a cutting. If this is so, geranium plants could be produced more reasonably from seed than from cuttings, and some of the disease problems could be reduced.

Hydrangea

The hydrangea is forced for Easter and Mother's Day. It is started from rooted cuttings made in the spring, the plants are grown outdoors during the summer, and after the leaves drop in the fall it is placed in cold storage for at least six weeks. The dormant plants then are brought into the greenhouse in late December for Easter forcing and in late January for Mother's Day forcing.

● **STEM TIP OR LEAF BUD CUTTINGS ARE
MADE FROM MARCH TO MAY**

Pruned shoots from the plants forced for the holidays can be used as a source of cuttings; however, for a dependable number of cuttings for a given time it is necessary to maintain a stock block of plants just for cuttings. Hydrangeas are opposite leaved, and to make leaf bud cuttings the stem is cut just above each pair of leaves. Then it is split through the middle of the stem so that each cutting has a leaf and split stem segment about 2 inches long. Hydrangea leaves are large and it may be necessary to trim the leaves to limit the water loss from the cutting. The cuttings must be kept moist at all times, and because of this it is best to use a mist system for rooting hydrangeas. If a mist system is not used the propagation bench will need to be shaded and the cuttings should be covered by moist cloth for the first few days. Leaf bud cuttings are perfectly satisfactory, and this is a method for getting the maximum number of plants from a limited number of cuttings. The cuttings root in about three weeks at 60° air temperature and 65° to 70° bench temperature. Coarse sand, perlite, or mixtures of perlite and peat can be used satisfactorily for rooting hydrangeas.

- HYDRANGEAS ARE GROWN OUTDOORS IN THE SUMMER

The rooted cuttings are potted in 3-inch pots and placed in a 60° house. New root growth should be seen a few days after potting, and an application of nitrogen fertilizer then should be made followed by another application in two weeks. After two or three weeks the 3-inch hydrangeas are shifted to 6-inch pots. When they are established in the 6-inch pots, they then are moved outdoors and grown under lath in May or early June. The plants develop larger leaves in the partial shade under lath than they do in full sun.

The hydrangea requires a great deal of water, and it is a big help to have a sprinkler system for general irrigation as well as misting the leaves periodically during the day.

Fertilizer should be applied regularly. The plants that are going to be finished with pink flowers should be given fertilizers high in phosphorus, and those that are to be finished with blue flowers should have no phosphorus as that ties up the aluminum that causes the blue color. Use 20-20-20, or similar analysis fertilizer, at 3 pounds per 100 gallons of water each two weeks for the pink hydrangeas; and 25-0-25 or similar analysis fertilizer, at 3 pounds per 100 gallons of water every two weeks for the blue ones.

The plants should be pinched about the middle of July. By that time the plant should be large enough so that the pinch can be made above at least two sets of good sized leaves. It is possible to root the pinched portion and grow it as a single stem (cane) plant.

- ### HYDRANGEAS NEED COOL STORAGE TO MATURE THE FLOWER BUD

Before frost in the fall the plants are moved to frames where they can be protected from freezing, and the plants should be watered and fertilized regularly during this period, too. About the first of November the plants are moved to dark storage where they can be kept at about 50°. The leaves drop after the plants have been in the dark for awhile, and should be removed to prevent the spread of disease. The plants may have to be watered while they are in storage, but they should not be kept wet.

- ### FORCING HYDRANGEAS

Varieties force at different rates, but at 60° it requires about thirteen weeks from the time the dormant plants are taken out of storage until they are in full flower. When Easter comes in March, the poinsettias are hardly cleared from the benches in time to start forcing hydrangeas. For later Easters the plants are brought in correspondingly later.

It is most important to get the root system started first. The plants will need to be watered, but the soil should not be kept constantly wet until new root growth is observed. If the plants have been grown in smaller pots, and are to be shifted to larger pots for finishing, they should be started in the small pots until root growth is good and then shifted. It is sometimes difficult to get new roots started in newly shifted plants. Dormant plants are usually started pot to pot and then spaced as needed to the final spacing of about 2 square feet per plant.

The fertilizer program should start as soon as root growth is good. The plants should be fertilized in the same way they were during the summer growing period, except the ones that are to be finished blue must be given three or four applications of aluminum sulfate at the rate of 1 pound per 5 gallons of water.

It is the pink hydrangea that is grown in quantity. Just a limited number of white ones are forced. Blue hydrangeas are more popular in some areas than others. The blue or pink flower is regulated by the fertilizer that is applied.

Hydrangeas are notorious for their water consumption. They need to be watered frequently or they wilt badly.

The most popular size hydrangea is three cane grown in 6-inch pots. One and two cane hydrangeas may be grown in 4- or 5-inch pots.

• HYDRANGEA TROUBLES

The two spotted mite (red spider) needs to be closely controlled on hydrangeas. It is best to use a weekly preventive spray during the summer, and be sure to give the plants a thorough spraying before they are put in the frame. Reinfestation apparently is not so rapid when the plants are in the greenhouse during the forcing period, and only occasional treatments should have to be given during forcing.

Bud rot in storage can be a problem, particularly on the variety Merveille. Be sure that leaves and other trash are cleaned up. Operate the storage as dry as possible, and provide constant air movement with air circulation fans.

Fig. 7—37. The hydrangea plant on the left was treated with the growth regulant chemical, B-Nine, and the plant on the right received no treatment. B-Nine can be used to reduce the height on some hydrangea varieties that grow too tall. (Naugatuck Chemical photograph)

Lily

As a potted plant the lily is grown only for Easter. The bulbs are produced primarily on the West Coast, they are dug in the fall, given treatments including six weeks at 33° before shipment as this promotes early flowering, and then shipped to the grower in November. Lilies are graded by circumference in inches from the small size of 6 to 7 inches to the large size of 10 to 11 inches. Generally the larger bulbs produce more flowers.

If the bulbs cannot be potted when they are received, they should be placed in refrigerated storage. Holding the bulbs at high temperatures for even short periods before potting can nullify the precooling effect and cause the bulbs to force slowly. Depending on the date of Easter, the bulbs are potted in late November or December and grown in a 60° house.

Fig. 7—38. Lily bulb production fields in Oregon. (From Kodachrome by C. F. Doucette)

It requires about seventeen weeks to force lilies. Flowering can be speeded by warmer temperatures and slowed in cooler temperatures. For sales at Easter the customer wants at least one flower open on the plant. In order to have the plants at just the right stage of development, it often requires considerable moving of the plants in order to keep them in the right temperature and the right stage of growth.

• FORCING EASTER LILIES

Lilies are subject to root diseases and poor root growth in waterlogged soils. Use steamed soil, and be sure that it is coarse and porous so that it drains well. Do not shred the soil, and add enough straw, strawy manure, or coarse peat to keep the soil loose and porous. Do not add phosphorus to lily soils, but add fine agricultural limestone, hydrated lime, or gypsum at the rate of a 5-inch pot per wheelbarrow of soil.

After planting the bulbs, pots should be placed in a 60° greenhouse and watered well. Root growth should be evident in a few days and the stem should break through the soil in about one week. Start the fertilizer program with the next watering. Use a low phosphorus fertilizer such as 25-5-20. If an injector is being used so that fertilizer is being added with each watering, 25-5-20 fertilizer or its equivalent should be used at the rate of about ½ pound per 100 gallons of water applied. If fertilizer is being applied periodically, the same fertilizer should be used at the rate of 3 pounds per 100 gallons of water, and an application made at least every two weeks.

The plants are started pot to pot and then spaced as needed. Be sure to space soon enough and adequately or the stems will be thin and tall. Lilies should be given as much sunlight as possible. Growing them in shaded locations or under dirty glass is almost sure to produce tall lilies.

• CROFT OR ACE LILIES ARE THE MOST POPULAR VARIETIES

Croft lilies are subject to some root diseases and some leaf troubles, and for those reasons Ace lilies often are used instead of Croft. The Ace flower is a bit smaller, and the leaves are shorter.

Georgia lilies are used for cut flowers, but some selections of the Georgia lilies are used successfully for potted Easter lilies. The Georgia lilies typically have longer stems and more flowers for the same size bulb than either Croft or Ace.

Six to seven weeks before Easter you should be able to feel flower buds in the leafy stem tip. If they cannot be felt, place the plants in a warmer greenhouse. At four weeks before Easter the flower buds should be about 2 inches long.

If the flowers develop too rapidly, the plants may be moved to cool storage. This should be done just before the first bud starts to open. They can be held in 50° storage for at least a week and still open satisfactorily when brought into warmer temperatures.

- **LILY BULBS ARE SOMETIMES POTTED IMMEDIATELY AFTER DIGGING**

In some areas of the country the bulbs are potted immediately after they are dug, and then grown during the fall in cold frames. Under this sytem the stems are heavier and shorter, the leaves larger and well developed right down to the pot, and there may be more flowers. However, this method requires more handling and some cold frame space for fall growing.

The potted bulbs are kept as cool as possible in the frames, but they are protected from freezing. Good root growth is made, and a compact rosette of leaves forms immediately above the soil. Bulbs handled in this way may force a little faster than bulbs that had storage before potting, but the same forcing procedures are used.

The West Coast growers who pot immediately after the bulbs are dug use Croft and Ace lilies mainly, and they pot after the bulbs are dug in October. Southern growers use southern-grown Georgia lilies, and they pot immediately after the bulbs are dug in late August or early September.

- **EASTER LILY TROUBLES**

Aphids can be troublesome, but they should be controlled rather easily if the plants are watched and treated when necessary.

Nematodes infest lilies, and they are associated with some of the root diseases of lilies. Be sure that the potting soil and handling equipment are steamed thoroughly; the benches and ground that the pots are set on should be steamed also.

Root rot is especially a problem in Croft lilies. Ace and Georgia lilies are not as susceptible to root rot, and those varieties should be grown if root rot has been common. Use a coarse, well-drained soil that is steam sterilized, and allow the soil to dry somewhat between waterings. If root rot does occur, a soil drench with a mixture of Terraclor 75 at ½ pound and Dexon 35 at ½ pound per 100 gallons of water should be used.

Loss of lower leaves may be due to root rot, lack of nitrogen fertilizer, or growing the plants too closely together.

If plants grow too tall or too short, this is most likely caused by temperature or light. Lilies forced at 50° usually are taller than those grown at 60°. Plants grown in full sunlight will be shorter than those grown in poor light or shaded conditions.

Fig. 7—39. A poinsettia stock plant field in southern California at time of harvest. Mr. Paul Ecke, Sr. in the photograph is the producer of poinsettia stock plants. (Paul Ecke, Inc., photograph)

Poinsettia

The poinsettia is the Christmas plant, and it is flowered for that season only. The stock plants are grown in southern California, and the dormant plants are shipped to the greenhouse growers in April. They are started in growth as soon as possible, the shoots are pinched during the summer, and the rooted cuttings are propagated in late August and September.

• START THE POINSETTIA STOCK PLANTS WARM AND MOIST

When the dormant stock plants are received they hardly look capable of supporting life; however, after planting they start in growth readily at 70° in a moist atmosphere. The soil should be allowed to dry somewhat between waterings, but the tops should be kept moist until there is good shoot development. It helps to cover the canes with moist burlap until shoots start to grow. The stock plants need to be planted in good, coarse soil and in large containers that drain readily. Root growth will not be good in water-logged soil. The plants are started out container to container, but when shoot growth starts in May they should be placed at their finish spacing, at least 2 feet by 2 feet.

If new field soil is used for planting the stock plants, superphosphate and calcium fertilizers should be mixed in with the soil before planting. After root growth starts in May regular fertilizer applications should be started. If a fertilizer injector is not used, weekly applications of 25-0-25 or 25-5-20 should be made at the rate of 2 pounds per 100 gallons of water. The soil needs to be well watered, and it helps to use a mulch of strawy manure or straw on the soil.

During the summer the stock plant should be pinched. The object is to provide the maximum number of cuttings for the best propagation period in late summer. Since it requires about four weeks from a pinch to the production of a new shoot that can be pinched, the first pinch needs to be made by late May, followed by pinches in late June and late July. This should give maximum cutting production for late August. The pinch should be made above two or more leaves.

The jumbo size stock plant will produce at least sixty cuttings per plant for the season, and the #1 stock plant about forty-five cuttings per plant.

- **THE DATE OF PROPAGATION DETERMINES THE SIZE OF THE PLANT WHEN IT IS FINISHED FOR CHRISTMAS**

Cuttings propagated in July could be finished as pinched plants, and cuttings propagated in early August can be finished in large pots and tubs as tall plants for cathedral and store decorations. The late August and early September propagation should furnish the right height plants for 6-inch and 7-inch pots. Poinsettias can be propagated as late as the middle of September; these plants are short, and are finished in smaller pots.

About a 4-inch cutting is used, and it roots in three weeks with 60° air temperature and 70° bench temperature. Since this is not the heating season in many areas, steam heat will probably not be available to maintain temperatures. Electric soil heating cables should be used in such instances as the cuttings will root very slowly if temperatures are not maintained. Poinsettias root well in either coarse sand or perlite. The cuttings are stuck about 2 inches apart in the row and the rows are spaced 5 inches. The cuttings should be removed from the bench when the roots are ½ inch long. A few of the cuttings probably will be barely callused when they are lifted. They can be restuck to complete rooting or they can be potted. In most instances callused cuttings root well in pots.

Poinsettia cuttings should be rooted under mist if possible. Generally a better job of rooting cuttings can be done under mist, but they do need to be furnished fertilizer—especially nitrogen—as the mist seems to leach the nitrogen out of the cutting. If fertilizer is not applied to cuttings under mist, growth can be slow after potting and a lower leaf or two may drop.

If a mist system is used the cuttings do not need to be shaded, or a very light shade is used. Without mist the cuttings must be heavily shaded so that they do not lose more water than they absorb. If possible it is best to remove some of the shade after one week as the cuttings will stretch if they are heavily shaded after they start to root.

If several batches of cuttings are to be propagated, the propagation bench should be steam sterilized before each lot is stuck.

Poinsettias can be rooted successfully directly in pots if a porous soil mixture is used. Peat or clay pots can be used for this direct rooting. Direct rooting in pots is best handled under a mist system.

The rooted cuttings are planted in 2¼-inch or 3-inch pots depending on how long they are going to be held before panning. New root growth should be observed within a week after potting, and regular fertilizer applications should be started. The potted plants are transplanted to larger pots in late September and early October. This is called panning, as the poinsettia pot is not as deep as the standard pot. Three plants are placed in a 6-inch pan, four plants in a 7-inch pan, and the larger pans have a correspondingly greater number of plants in them.

- **POINSETTIAS ARE GROWN AT 60° NIGHT TEMPERATURE AND 65° TO 70° DAY TEMPERATURES**

It is possible to increase this temperature a few degrees if the crop is slow; however, reducing the temperature late in the season to delay the plants can cause root rot and leaf drop.

- **WATERING OF POINSETTIAS IS VERY CRITICAL**

This problem is not nearly as great with coarse, porous soils as it is with fine, heavy soils. Poinsettias are susceptible to root and stem diseases that are promoted by water-logged conditions. Be sure that the soil dries somewhat between waterings. At about the middle of the poinsettia forcing period there often is a natural but radical change in weather conditions. The early fall is typically hot and bright, and then in late October or November the weather changes to cool and dark. If the watering practices do not change as rapidly and as completely, the soil will remain too wet, and the diseases may get their start.

- **FLOWERING OF THE POINSETTIA IS AFFECTED BY THE LENGTH OF DAY**

It flowers in short days, and remains leafy and vegetative in long days. In natural conditions the flower starts to form the last week in

September, and it is developed fully about three months later—just in time for Christmas if everything works right. More commonly it flowers a bit early for Christmas in natural conditions. To prevent too early flowering many growers give their poinsettias artificially long days by lighting them each night for two hours from September 20 to October 5, which delays flowering. The same lighting system used for mums can be used for poinsettias.

Actually poinsettias are very sensitive to light, and great care needs to be taken not to light them accidentally later in the fall. Several cases are known in which poinsettias have been kept from flowering in the vicinity of an alley lamp, and it is not unusual for some of the plants to fail to flower in the vicinity of the thermometer simply because the light is located there and the night man turns it on before entering the house to read the temperature and turns it off on leaving. That is sufficient light to prevent flowering in the poinsettia. Reflected light from the chrysanthemum area also can cause a problem. Many homeowners wonder why their poinsettia grows so well

Fig. 7—40. The poinsettia on the left was treated with the growth regulant chemical, B-Nine, and the plant on the right was not treated. (Naugatuck Chemical photograph)

and looks so good, but has never flowered since the first Christmas when they received it. They do not realize that they are preventing it from flowering by turning on the lights in their home each night.

In spite of trying to propagate poinsettias on just the right day so they will finish at the right height for Christmas, situations develop that lead to plants that are taller than desired. The stock plants do not crop completely, and some cuttings are taken earlier in August when they are ready. Then, too, if two or three propagation dates are used, the work is spread out so that it can be handled better. Plans are made on the basis of average weather conditions with the realization that during this particular year the weather may be below average and the plants will not grow as well. The tendency then is to propagate a little

Fig. 7—41. The poinsettia on the left was treated wtih the growth regulant chemical, Cycocel, and the plant on the right was not treated. (American Cyanamid Co. photograph)

earlier than necessary to allow for delay. This produces taller poinsettias than desired, unless growth regulant chemicals are used to keep the plants within height limitations. They have been used very successfully, but the decision to use them must be made before October 15, and sometimes it is not possible to know at that time whether or not the plants are going to finish too tall. If they are used later than that, the flower may be reduced in size and deformed. Cycocel is used at the rate of 1 quart per 10 gallons of water, and then it is drenched on the soil at the rate of 2 fluid ounces per 2¼-inch pot or 6 fluid ounces per 6-inch pan. The plants can be treated in the small pots and then again after they are panned if it appears that they are going to be too high. The treated plants should be shorter, with heavier stems and greener foliage.

• MOST POINSETTIAS ARE GROWN SINGLE STEM

Poinsettia pans with three or four flowers are the most popular size. These are grown by planting three or four plants per pot and letting each plant produce a flower. Poinsettias can be pinched to produce two or more flowers per stem, but this requires a little longer growing period, the stems are not as strong, and the flowers are smaller. If a hard pinch is used, it should be made about August 15. Soft pinches should be made about September 1.

Poinsettias need a continuous supply of fertilizer. If superphosphate and calcium fertilizers are used in potting soil, fertilizers such as 25-0-25 or 25-5-20 are suitable. Adding some fertilizer with each watering by means of a fertilizer injector is a good way to make sure of a constant supply of fertilizer. If an injector is not used, fertilizer should be applied at least every two weeks at the rate of 3 pounds of 25-0-25 or equivalent per 100 gallons of water.

In some areas, at the time of panning, a fern is placed at the middle of the pan. This practice is used to provide some coverage at the base of the plant so if the bottom leaves dropped the bare stems would not be so evident. Fern in the poinsettia pan is not a common practice as it is no improvement for a well grown poinsettia.

Poinsettias should be staked. It is best to place a wire stake by each stem and tie to it. The wire stakes are enameled green so they are not noticeable, and they can be bent easily to position the stem at the right angle.

The flowers do need to be protected in shipment. Tissue paper is wrapped around each flower, or a specially designed paper with adhesive on each end is formed in a protective cylinder around each flower. If the plants then are placed in paper sleeves they can be moved rapidly and safely.

- **THE RED POINSETTIA IS THE MOST POPULAR**

Most customers associate red poinsettias with Christmas. White and pink varieties also are available, but their use has been limited. Actually all poinsettia flowers are yellow, and these flowers are located at the center of colorful red, pink, or white bracts.

- **CAREFUL DISEASE CONTROL MEASURES**
  SHOULD BE USED WITH POINSETTIAS

The white fly is the most common pest on poinsettias. Its control is not difficult, but it should be eradicated in the early stages of the plant's growth. The flowers are bleached easily by insecticides later in the season, and if spray is used the residues can be unsightly.

Rhizoctonia, Pythium, or Thielaviopsis can be a problem with poinsettias at any time from the propagation bench to the finish pan. Propagation bench, soil, used pots, benches, and handling equipment need to be thoroughly steam sterilized. Thielaviopsis develops more easily at temperatures below 60°, and this is one of the reasons why it is hazardous to drop temperatures late in the season. The most common symptoms are loss of roots and loss of the lower leaves. Both Rhizoctonia and Pythium get started more easily in constantly wet soils. Use good porous soils that drain well for poinsettias, and water carefully. It may not be possible to identify the disease by merely looking at the plant. It is best to have the plant inspected by a pathologist for positive identification of the disease as each disease is controlled by a different material. Ferbam is used for Thielaviopsis, Dexon or Morsodren for Pythium, and Terraclor or Morsodren for Rhizoctonia. Since Rhizoctonia and Pythium are quite common on poinsettias, many growers use a preventive drench of Morsodren or a mixture of Dexon and Terraclor. The best time to use this drench is shortly after the plants are panned.

Many things get blamed for the loss of lower leaves on poinsettias, and no doubt several situations can cause leaf drop. The most common causes of leaf drop on poinsettias are lack of nitrogen or lack of water in the plant because of lack of roots. The most common causes of lack of roots are root diseases or poorly aerated soils. Use a coarse, porous soil for poinsettias, and the root growth will be better, there will be less root diseases, and the bottom leaves will stay on the plant.

CHAPTER 8

Troubles, Pests, and Diseases

CHAPTER 8

Most of the problems that are encountered in plant growth are caused by common and ordinary events of some kind. Look first for the simple things that may have occurred to cause a particular problem. Don't assume that all of the routine procedures were performed properly until after they have been checked carefully. Try to determine if this sort of trouble might be associated with something that took place in the soil, or if the cause of the trouble was more likely to have reached the plant through the air.

• COMPARE THE PLANT TROUBLE WITH UNAFFECTED PLANTS

It is always good to be able to determine if similar plants in your greenhouse or in neighboring greenhouses are affected in the same way. If they are not, then search for the difference in treatment.

• LOOK FOR A PATTERN

Very often the pattern of the trouble will point to the cause. It is important to observe whether it happens only in certain areas of the bench, on a certain part of the plant, or is scattered throughout the planting. If the trouble occurs on only one variety or at only one stage of plant growth, this fact may indicate the cause.

Even without knowing just what conditions have been furnished the plants, it is possible to "read back" on the stems, leaves, and roots of the plant and determine if the general conditions for growth have been good. A plant that has small leaves and short, hard growth will react much differently than one that has large leaves and soft, vigorous growth. Compare the leaf and stem growth with the root growth. It is impossible to get decent top growth on plants without roots, but it is possible to have poor top growth and an excellent root system. If the root system is poor, the most common causes are too fine or too heavy soil with resulting poor drainage and poor air conditions in the soil; keeping the soil constantly wet; too much fertilizer in the soil; or some pest or disease infesting the roots.

- **MAKE A LIST OF WHAT HAS BEEN DONE DURING THE TIME THE TROUBLE HAS BEEN SUSPECTED**

If a soil test has not been made recently, have one made at once and compare this with past tests. Very often trends that can be observed by looking at several tests on the same soil are more meaningful than the results from one test. Rather rapid changes can be expected in nitrogen; however, if all the tests indicate a low nitrogen supply, deficient amounts of nitrogen should be suspected. Phosphorus, pH, soluble salts, and calcium values remain quite constant, and if some sudden change is indicated by a soil test this would be associated with an unusual occurrence such as over-dose of fertilizer. Sometimes the person making the application uses the wrong bag of fertilizer, and sometimes the wrong amounts are used.

Make a review of the weather conditions. It may be possible that the trouble is associated with an extremely hot spell, or it could be caused by failure to change heating or watering practices with a change to cooler and darker weather.

It is very necessary to treat plants for pests and diseases, but it must be considered that some of the materials used can be toxic to plants. List all of the pest or disease control applications that have been made together with the exact materials that were used and the amount. It is helpful also to know what the weather conditions were at the time of the application. Keep in mind that a wettable powder of an insecticide may be perfectly safe, while the same insecticide as an emulsion may have a bad effect on plants in the greenhouse. Many mistakes are made in the amounts of material that are used on plants.

Make sure that the lighting and heating have been provided as scheduled, and don't forget that the work crew is around only about one third of the time. Plants grow—or at least they should grow—night and day and on holidays and week-ends. Give careful consideration to that two thirds of the time when the regular crew is not on duty.

It is helpful to discuss the situation with another individual. Another grower in the area may have a fresh view on the matter, or possibly the county agricultural agent can give some advice.

• SOME TROUBLES AND SOME POSSIBLE CAUSES

If the plant is not making any top growth, it is most likely that the plant does not have any roots. An infestation of symphilids could be the cause as they feed on roots, and in some instances they will eat the roots as rapidly as they grow. Symphilids may be difficult to find as they are small and when the soil is disturbed they scurry rapidly in order to stay in moist surroundings. More commonly the lack of roots is caused by water-logged soil or an over-supply of fertilizer. The soil situation will have to be corrected before the roots will grow, and nothing can be done about the top growth until the plant has a good root system.

Short growth in plants is usually related to a poor root system or to a lack of nitrogen. If the short growth is caused by a deficiency of nitrogen, the root system may be in good condition. Some plants are permanently stunted by even a short period without nitrogen in the early stages of growth. In either instance the leaves of the plant are usually small. With a nitrogen shortage the leaves are light or pale green, but a plant with poor roots has dull green leaves and often some of them are yellow.

Small leaves indicate a lack of nitrogen or of water in the plant. This lack may be caused by failure to supply water or nitrogen as needed, but it can be caused by poor root growth and the inability of the plant to take in as much water or nitrogen as needed. During the summer, plants that are partially shaded will have larger leaves than plants that are in full sun. Stems and leaves that originate from the soft, new growth on plants will be larger than shoots that come from the older and harder portions of the plant. Plants that are pinched soft or in the new growth of the stem tip will produce shoots with larger leaves than those that are pinched lower into the harder part of the stem.

Chlorosis, or yellowing of the leaves at the stem tip, is an indication of iron deficiency in the plant. This may be caused by a lack of nitrogen in the soil, by soil that is too alkaline or too acid, or by poor root growth and the inability to take enough iron into the plant. The most common cause of chlorosis is poor root growth resulting from water-logged soils or roots damaged by symphilids or nematodes. Check first to make sure that the roots are growing actively. Then if the pH is in a suitable range (about 5.5 to 6.5), an application of iron to the soil can restore the green color to the leaves.

Yellow leaves toward the base of the plant are an indication of a lack of nitrogen in the plant or a lack of light on those leaves caused by shading from the upper leaves or shading from closely spaced plants.

Small flowers often are blamed onto poor light conditions. This could be a contributing factor, but it is more probable that the flower size indicates a shortage of water or nitrogen in the plant. During the summer the use of high-pressure mist or pad and fan cooling reduces water loss (transpiration) from the plant, and flower size is increased. During the winter water loss from the plant can be high because of the dry air in the greenhouse at that time of the year, and high-pressure mist will help reduce transpiration at that time of the year also. The amount of water and nitrogen in the plant is directly related to the amount of root growth that the plant is making.

Leaf spots often indicate disease; however, they can be the result of foliar nematode or damage from an insecticide or fungicide. Foliar nematodes are not a common problem, and they usually develop a characteristic wedge-shaped dead area in the leaf. Many of the chemicals that are used for treating pests or diseases are harmful to plants if they are used improperly. They should not be used stronger or more often than recommended by the manufacturer. If the recommendations on the package are for outdoor crops only, seek good advice before using the material because it may be used at only half the strength in the greenhouse. Emulsions are more likely to cause leaf spots than wettable powders. Some gases such as sulfur dioxide or flue gases can cause leaf spots. This problem arises sometimes in highly industrial areas, but it can occur because of faulty operation of the greenhouse heating system.

Loss of the tip of the stem is a rather uncommon occurrence. When this occurs, side shoots start to grow in the same way as though the plant had been pinched, and quite often the loss of the stem tip is not actually noticed until after the appearance of the side shoots. Sometimes pests destroy or injure the stem tip. Tarnished plant bug injures the stem tip on mums, causing the loss of the tip. Grasshoppers and mice occasionally eat the stem tips. Some insecticides or fungicides may cause the loss of the stem tip, although it may not be the chemical itself but the material in which the chemical is dissolved. Some plants

Fig. 8—1. Leaf drop is a common problem of roses. It occurs primarily during the winter, and it may be associated with any adverse conditions for the rose plants' growth. Some pesticides cause severe leaf drop.

may be affected much more severely than others. A deficiency of boron in the plant can cause some stem tip problems. If boron deficiency is suspected, have this shortage verified by someone who is acquainted with the use of boron on greenhouse crops. Some boron is needed for many of the greenhouse plants, but not a great amount is required and trouble can also occur from an oversupply.

Wilting indicates that there is a lack of water in the plant, and it can be remedied by getting more water into the plant or by reducing the loss of water from the plant. Newly planted cuttings wilt for a few days until there is enough root growth to supply the plant with sufficient water. It is good practice to reduce the water loss from newly planted cuttings by misting them or increasing the air moisture (humidity) around the cuttings. The water loss from the cuttings can be reduced also by placing some cloth above the cuttings to reduce the amount of light on them. If older plants wilt this may indicate that the soil is dry or that the roots are unable to take up water. The most common causes of root damage are water-logged soil, oversupply of fertilizer, or nematodes. In some instances wilting indicates the presence of a disease that interferes with the movement of water in the plant.

Weak stems on plants often may be related to poor light conditions during the winter or to a combination of poor light and high temperatures. However, it is possible that there is a deficiency of carbon dioxide for periods during the day, and the addition of carbon dioxide to the atmosphere may help some plants. Constant air circulation brings new air in contact with the leaves, and the plant is supplied better with carbon dioxide. Plants are often spaced farther apart during the winter so there will be less shading of one plant by another.

There are many causes of marginal leaf burn, but some of the more common are the excessive use of fertilizer, the effect of some insecticides or fungicides on certain plants, and any severe injury to the roots that limits the intake of water into the plant.

Twisted or malformed shoots are an indication of the presence of weed killers in or around the greenhouse. There have been many sad instances of the improper or careless use of weed killers around greenhouse plants and flowers. Almost any weed killer has the potential to kill the crop plants, too, but the weed killer that probably has done the most damage is 2, 4-D. This is a highly volatile material, and the fumes can affect plants a long distance from the place where the weed killer was used. It is effective in very small amounts, and great damage has been done simply by using in the greenhouse a sprayer that had been used outdoors for spraying weeds. Greenhouse plants have been damaged by 2, 4-D from lumber used for benches that came from a lumber yard where the weeds were sprayed with 2, 4-D and where accidentally some spray also drifted onto the lumber. Be careful of lawn and garden fertilizers that contain 2, 4-D. They may have the same or similar fertilizer analysis as some of the fertilizers used around the greenhouse, but if they contain a weed killer in addition to the fertilizer, the greenhouse plants can be seriously damaged or killed.

Weeds in the greenhouse do need to be controlled, but it must be done in such a way that the crop plants are not damaged. Steam sterilization controls weeds in the bench. Weeds under the bench are controlled best with either sodium arsenite or karmex. Be sure that only the weeds are sprayed as the spray will damage the crop plants if it hits them. Use a coarse spray so that the spray is not carried onto the plants in the bench by wind currents. Sodium arsenite and karmex do not give off fumes that will damage the greenhouse plants; however, it is always possible to get into trouble if the weed killer is sprayed on the heating lines.

Insects can cause misshapen or malformed flowers. Many insects could be involved, but the ones most commonly guilty are either aphids or thrips. Aphids are active at any time of the year, but thrips sail into the greenhouse from outdoor, seasonal crops primarily in early summer and again in late summer. Improper temperatures can be the cause of malformed flowers on mums, poinsettias, and carnations, and temperatures or fluctuating day length can produce malformed flowers on mums.

Failure of shoots to develop and grow may be associated with hard growth on plants. Usually plants that are soft and in active growth will break more readily, and the growth of the shoots will be more rapid. Some varieties produce shoots more reluctantly than others after a pinch; however, most plants break more readily when the pinch is made in the new growth. Plants with poor root systems or which are poorly fertilized will not produce shoots well. Some insecticides harden the growth of plants and cause poor breaking.

Flowering too early or too late may be due to the amount of sunlight or temperature. Some plants are affected more than others. Snapdragons and carnations flower much more rapidly in bright sun and high temperatures than they do in dark weather and cool temperatures. Benches that are in the shade of a gutter do not flower as soon as benches that are in good light. If the black cloth used to shade mums is stored in the same location above the plants each day, the plants in this shade flower later than the plants that are not shaded. Because of the better light conditions at the side of the bench, plants at the edge of the bench flower a little sooner than the plants toward the center of the bench. Flowering in some plants is delayed in extremely hot weather.

Fig. 8—2. A gutter to the south reduces the amount of light for several feet in the greenhouse. The chrysanthemums in this bench show the effects of this light reduction. Growth is slower on the gutter side of the bench and flowering is later.

● CONSTANT ATTENTION IS NEEDED TO KEEP
   PESTS UNDER CONTROL

Pests can multiply rapidly, and if they are not controlled in the early stages of an infestation they can be very damaging. There is some difference of opinion whether a regular preventive control program should be used, or the plants watched carefully and the pests controlled when they first appear. If there is any question about not being able to observe the plants closely, a preventive control program should be used. For a preventive program, treating the plants once a month should be often enough; however, at times it will be necessary to make more frequent applications.

Very often each control material will be effective on only one or a few pests. It is very important to identify which pest is present, and

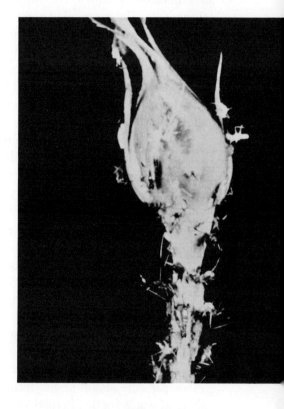

Fig. 8—3. Aphids on a rose stem. (From a Kodachrome by The Ohio State University Extension Service)

then to use the best material for the control of that pest. The effectiveness of control materials or methods changes, and it is necessary to be well informed continually of the best control measures to use.

Aphids locate on stem tips rather than on the lower parts of plants. The control material must be applied so that good coverage and penetration of the tip results. The aphid problem is more severe on chrysanthemums than on other crops, but aphids can infest most greenhouse plants. Effective controls are Meta Systox-R used at the rate of 1½ pints per 100 gallons of water; Dibrom 8 vaporized from the steam lines at the rate of 1 fluid ounce per 10,000 cubic feet; Vapona 2 vaporized from the steam lines at the rate of 2 fluid ounces per 10,000 cubic feet; or Vapona aerosol.

Cyclamen mites are not a common problem. They are found sometimes on cyclamen, ivy, African violets, snapdragons, and a few other plants. The mites infest the leaves at the tip of the plant causing a cupping or puckering of the leaves. They also stop the growth of the leaves. Cyclamen mites are very tiny and cannot be seen without the aid of a strong lens. Controls include Endrin 18½% emulsion at the rate of 1 quart per 100 gallons of water; Kelthane 18½% emulsion at 1 pint per 100 gallons of water; or Thiodan 50 at 1 pound per 100 gallons of water.

There are several kinds of leafrollers and the material that controls one may not be effective on the others. Controls are Sevin 50 at the rate of 1 pound per 100 gallons of water; Zectran 2 used at the rate of 1½ quarts per 100 gallons of water; or Vapona 2 at the rate of 2 fluid ounces per 10,000 cubic feet vaporized from the steam lines.

Nematodes mainly infest the roots. They interfere with the uptake of water and fertilizer by the plant, and the top portion of the plant can have the same appearance that it would have if the roots were injured by other causes. Shoot growth is short and hard, leaves are small and their color is dull, the plants wilt easily, and the leaves drop prematurely. For control, soil and handling equipment must be carefully sterilized before planting; plants that are brought in from other locations must be free of nematodes; infested plants may be treated by drenching the soil with Nemagon E.C. 2 at the rate of 2 gallons per acre of soil or VC-13 used at the rate of 1 quart per 100 gallons of water applied to each 400 square feet of soil.

Red spider (two spotted mite) is the pest that is found most commonly in the greenhouse. It may be on any of the upper parts of plants, but very often it is located on the under side of the lower leaves. Red spiders are tiny, and the damage that they do is more evident than they are themselves. Their feeding on the under side of the leaf causes a white and green, speckled appearance on the upper surface of the leaf. To be effective for the control of red spider the pesticide must give good coverage to the underside of the lower leaves. Controls include Pentac 50 used at the rate of ½ pound per 100 gallons of water; Aramite 15 used at the rate of 1¼ pound per 100 gallons of water; Tedion 25 used at the rate of 1 pound per 100 gallons of water.

Slugs stay in moist locations during the day and they come out to feed on the plants at night. They eat either leaves or petals. For control, use Slugit at the rate of 1 fluid ounce per 1 gallon of water, or Zectran 2 used at the rate of 5 pints per 100 gallons of water.

Thrips can sail with the wind for long distances, and when thrips are plentiful outdoors they reinfest the plants in the greenhouse about as soon as they are treated. Thrips are small and not easily noticed because they stay in shaded or moist locations. The damage that they cause is however quite noticeable. They inhabit the flowers primarily and produce streaks on the petals. If the infestation is great enough, they may cause so much damage to the flower that it will be crippled and may not open. During the thrips season they are found on roses, carnations, and chrysanthemums. To control thrips, spray the tops of the plants; treatment will need to be often as reinfestation from outdoors can be continuous. Use Dieldrin 18.5% at the rate of 1 quart per 100 gallons of water; Dibrom 8 vaporized from steam pipes at the rate of 1 fluid ounce per 10,000 cubic feet; or Diazinon 50 at 1 pound per 100 gallons of water.

White flies are seasonal pests on mums, tomatoes, ageratum, and poinsettias. They are located on the under side of the leaves. Controls include Thiodan 50 at the rate of 1 pound per 100 gallons of water (the Thiodan vapor is effective in controlling white fly, and the spray may be directed at the bench or pot and still affect the pest on the under side of leaf); Dibrom 8 vaporized from the steam lines at the rate of 1 fluid ounce per 10,000 cubic feet; and Meta Systox-R used at the rate of 1½ pints per 100 gallons of water.

• DISEASES CAN BE CAUSED BY FUNGI, BACTERIA OR VIRUSES

It is the growth of the disease organisms—fungi, bacteria, or viruses—in or on the plant that causes disease. In some instances the organism grows so rapidly that it clogs the water or food conducting tissues of the plant. In other instances the disease organism feeds on the plant tissues, causing a rot or decay. Some disease organisms live within the plant, and others exist on the surface of the plant.

Plants that are growing well are not as susceptible to disease organisms as plants that are in a poor state of health. Providing the best growing conditions for the plants is the best defense against disease.

Eliminate the disease organisms in the surroundings by careful sterilization with steam. Be sure that soil, benches, pots, and all handling equipment are sterilized. Then be sure that disease organisms are not brought in from outside the greenhouse. The propagation stock must be free of disease. Culture-indexing is the best method to eliminate disease in the propagation stock.

Many of the disease organisms get their start in growth and thrive in constantly moist situations. Prevent constantly moist soils by using

Fig. 8—4. Chemical sterilization of geranium fields in California (Grand View Geranium Gardens photograph)

coarse, porous soil mixtures and spacing waterings well. Moisture on the leaves and flowers can be eliminated by providing better air circulation and by using heat properly.

Plants can look diseased when they are in poor growing conditions. Make sure that you know what the problem is with the plant before you treat it. Correct the cultural conditions before any further treatment is made. Many of the diseases produce somewhat similar symptoms in plants, but the treatments may be different. Make sure that the treatment used is the best one for the disease that the plant has. It is best to get some professional help to definitely determine which disease is present. This help can be obtained through the county agricultural agent or the state florists' association.

• STEM AND ROOT DISEASES

These organisms or spores of the organisms are common in the soil and on equipment used around a greenhouse. Steam sterilization of the soil and equipment in the greenhouse is essential. When steam is not available, the best means of chemical sterilization must be used.

Growth of these disease organisms in the soil is much more rapid in soils that are constantly wet and poorly aerated. It is possible to prevent a serious disease problem just by using good soil mixtures and using water properly.

In propagating plants, care must be taken that disease is not propagated also. Propagation stock must be carefully selected and observed closely for evidence of disease. Culture-indexing of the propagation stock can eliminate some of the diseases from the stock.

Rhizoctonia is the most common stem rot, and it can affect just about any plant grown in the greenhouse. It usually occurs with young plants rather than the older ones, and the typical Rhizoctonia stem rot produces a rotted area at the soil line. Plants that are planted deeply are much more subject to Rhizoctonia than those that are planted shallow. Spacing waterings well and providing the maximum air circulation so that the soil surface dries readily help to control Rhizoctonia. Terraclor 75 at ½ pound per 100 gallons of water or Morsodren at 3 fluid ounces per 100 gallons of water drenched on the soil at the rate of 1 quart per square foot of soil controls the spread of

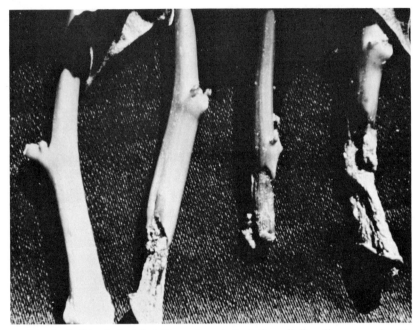

Fig. 8—5. Rhizoctonia infestations often start at the soil line. Here are poinsettia cuttings that show the results of Rhizoctonia. (From a Kodachrome by C. W. Ellett)

Rhizoctonia through the soil. Drench the base of the plant as well as the soil.

Pythium stem and root rot can occur on geraniums, chrysanthemums, poinsettias, some foliage plants, and several bedding plants. Some chrysanthemum varieties are much more susceptible to Pythium than others, and their use is limited because of this. Either the roots or the stem can be attacked by Pythium, which grows rapidly in poorly aerated and constantly moist situations. The spread of Pythium in the soil can be controlled with Dexon 35 at ½ pound per 100 gallons of water or Morsodren at 3 fluid ounces per 100 gallons of water drenched on the soil at the rate of 1 quart per square foot of soil.

Fusarium diseases can affect several greenhouse plants, but the most serious problem is with carnations. Fusarium wilt is caused by a Fusarium organism growing in the inner tissues of the stem of the carnation plant. It produces wilting and eventual death of the plant. Usually in the final stages of the disease the base of the stem is rotted at the soil line, but the roots may appear to be in good condition. The only means of control are thorough sterilization of soil and equipment, and the elimination of the organism from propagation stock through culture-indexing.

Carnations are plagued also with a Fusarium stem rot disease. This Fusarium operates from the surface of the stem, and it produces the rot at a cut or break in the stem tissues. It can be a serious disease in the propagation bench, producing rot at the base of the cuttings and preventing the growth of roots. Fusarium stem rot also grows in the stem after flowers are cut, causing rot and wilting of various stems of the plant until the whole plant may be involved. Regular spraying of the carnation plants with Captan 50 at 1 pound per 100 gallons of water will help to eliminate this organism.

Verticillium wilt can occur in roses and snapdragons, but the major problem is with chrysanthemums. This disease threatened to eliminate the chrysanthemum industry until a culture-indexing method was devised that eliminated the disease organism from the chrysanthemum stock. The Verticillium organism grows in the inner tissues of the stem, producing the wilt symptoms shortly before the plant flowers. The only means of control is thorough sterilization of the soil and the elimination of the organism from the stock by culture-indexing.

Botrytis blight commonly affects many of the greenhouse plants, causing rot of leaves or petals. It also can produce stem rots; the plants most commonly affected are geranium and snapdragon. Botrytis stem rot of geranium starts in a wound or cut on the stem, and it produces a dark-brown rotted area. On snapdragons the Botrytis infestation occurs on the stem several inches above the soil level. The stem may be entirely girdled, and the portion of the plant above the infestation wilts. Botrytis also can be the cause of rot in the chrysanthemum propagation bench. The Botrytis organism is common in greenhouses, and if it is not eliminated it grows readily when conditions are suitable. Steam sterilize the soil, benches, and handling equipment thoroughly to eliminate the Botrytis organism. Use maximum ventilation and air circulation fans as this helps to keep the leaves and stem free of moisture. Spacing plants better will improve the air circulation around each plant, too. Either zineb or Botran can be used as a spray or dust for controlling Botrytis.

There are several bacterial diseases of greenhouse plants, but the most common ones are bacterial leaf spot and stem rot of geranium and bacterial wilt of carnations. These bacterial disease organisms live in the inner tissues of the plants. The bacterial leaf spot and stem rot organism that affects geraniums causes a leaf spot followed by the loss of foliage. The leaf spots may be small and circular or they may be

Fig. 8—6. Excessive growth of the Botrytis organism on snapdragon stems. (From a Kodachrome by C. W. Ellett)

wedge-shaped and at the margin of the leaf. The stem rot from this bacterial disease of geraniums is a brown-black rot. Cuttings infected with this organism do not root. The organism that causes bacterial wilt in carnations produces a general wilting of the carnation plant and a rotted area at the soil line. Usually the roots are rotted, too. The symptoms of bacterial wilt of carnations are easily confused with the symptoms of either Fusarium wilt or Rhizoctonia stem rot. Have the disease identified by a qualified person so that the right means of control can be used. Use cuttings that have been taken from culture-indexed stock.

• LEAF AND FLOWER DISEASES

Botrytis grows more readily on old, dying, or dead plant tissues, and it gets its start in cuts or in moist locations. Botrytis blight of chrysanthemum petals during hot and humid weather is common. It occurs on the tips of the oldest petals. Other flowers can be infested with Botrytis. Botrytis may attack older geranium florets and then the disease is spread to the leaves when the florets drop on them. For the control of Botrytis it is important to remove plant refuse from the greenhouse rapidly to eliminate a breeding place for the disease organism. Avoid moist and humid conditions by spacing the plants well, providing maximum ventilation, and heating while ventilating.

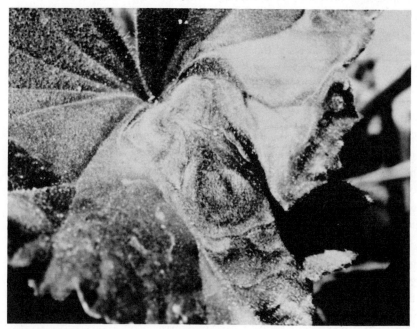

Fig. 8—7. The results of a Botrytis infestation on geranium leaves. (From a Koda-chrome by C. W. Ellett)

Continuous air movement with air circulation fans keeps the surface of the plant drier and less suitable for the growth of Botrytis. Mist-spraying or dusting with zineb can help control Botrytis, but must be done often to keep the new growth protected. Residue on the flowers and leaves from the spray or dust is objectionable, and every effort should be made first to eliminate Botrytis by controlling the air moisture and air movement around the plant.

Powdery mildew is a constant threat to rose plants. It is known most commonly by the powdery-white growth on the upper surface of the leaves, and it also produces puckering of the leaf. Powdery mildew is found sometimes on the stems and flowers of roses. The stem infestation has the characteristic white powder appearance, but on the petal the area involved may look brown and shiny with some twisting or puckering of the petal. Powdery mildew can occur on other plants such as chrysanthemum or snapdragon, but this is rather unusual. Apparently powdery mildew can start in growth with the slightest film of moisture on the leaves, stems, or petals. The best control is to regulate the heat and ventilation in such a way that there is constant air movement around the plants, with the plants kept warmer than the surrounding air. During the heating season it should be possible to stay away from powdery mildew infestations by turning the heat into the houses before the sun goes down and continuing to heat until the sun is well up. During the spring, summer, and fall there are times when heat is not available, and it is then difficult to control mildew. Sulfur is a standard control for mildew. It can be vaporized from steam lines or from fumers that are made for that specific purpose. To be effective, sulfur applications must be made at least three times a week. Either Karathane or Actidione PM used as a spray can give some control of powdery mildew, but they may be somewhat toxic to some plants.

Rust is more of a problem on carnations than on the other greenhouse plants, but it is quite rare even on carnations. In order to germinate, the rust spores need to have free water, and when carna-tions are grown entirely inside good greenhouses there should be no water on the leaves for any length of time. If there is rust on the plants, check the roof for leaks or drips. When an infestation of rust gets a start it is difficult to stop. It may be necessary to remove some

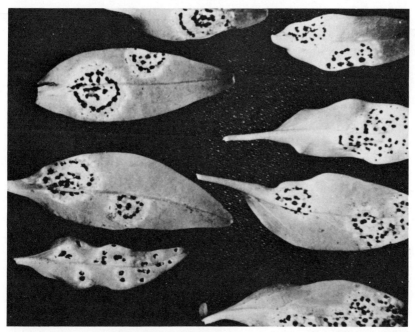

Fig. 8—8. A rust infestation on snapdragon leaves. (From a Kodachrome by C. W. Ellett)

of the most infested leaves from the plant, being careful not to scatter the spores on other plants. Spraying the plants with either zineb or captan helps to control rust, but applications must be made at least weekly.

Septoria leaf spot may affect chrysanthemums, carnations, and azaleas. It is more prevalent on plants that have been grown outdoors. Moisture on the leaves and high humidity provide ideal conditions for the start of septoria leaf spot. Keeping the foliage dry will limit this disease. Outdoor plantings, and indoor plantings showing some septoria, should be sprayed weekly with either ferbam, zineb, or captan.

There are many different virus diseases, and the effects of these diseases can be quite different. The chrysanthemum stunt disease threatened to bring the chrysanthemum industry to a halt until methods were found for culture-indexing chrysanthemum stock for virus and producing cuttings that are free from virus. There are several virus diseases of chrysanthemum, carnation, and geranium. It is possible to eliminate some of these from propagating stock by careful observation and selection of stock plants, but to be entirely certain the stock must be culture-indexed for virus. There are no known controls for virus other than selection of virus-free stock and prevention of reinfestation by insects or by those working with the plants.

- **USE THE BEST METHOD FOR GETTING THE CONTROL MATERIAL ON THE PLANT AT THE RIGHT TIME**

Several different methods can be used for applying pesticides and fungicides. Whatever the method that is used, the purpose is to get complete coverage of the plant or the pests with the right amount of

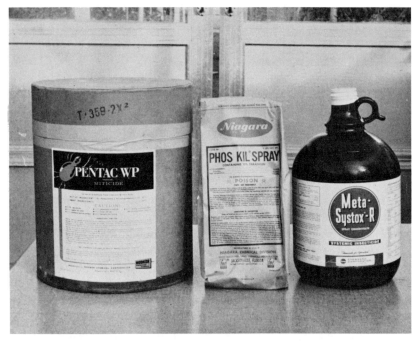

Fig. 8—9. Be sure to read the label of pesticides very carefully, and use the right material for the pest that is giving the trouble. Pesticides can be toxic to human beings or to plants, and the care that needs to be used is listed on the label. Pesticides well chosen and wisely used are indispensable, but carelessness in selection of material or in the way that it is used is costly. (Jednak Floral Co. photograph)

control material. The first concern is the welfare of the people using the material, second is the welfare of the plants, and then the effectiveness of the material in controlling the pest or disease. Many of the control materials are toxic to human beings and they must be used in such a way that they do not endanger anyone. It is possible for control materials to harm plants. In some instances the effect may be slight, and in others the plant may be damaged greatly. The effect of each material on each kind of plant must be known before it is used, as it is useless to control the pest or disease if the plant is going to be ruined in the process. It is best to be prepared to use more than one type of application as one method is often better than another in different situations.

One of the most common means of applying pest or disease controls in the greenhouse is with hydraulic sprayers. The recommended amount of control material is mixed with the water in the sprayer, and the sprayer pumps the mixture out at pressures of 200 to 400 pounds per square inch. At this pressure when proper nozzles are used the spray is very fine and gives good coverage of plants. A spreader or detergent can be used with the spray to provide better flow over the leaves. The amount of spreader to use varies with the hardness of the water and the plants being sprayed. If the spray remains in droplets on the leaves, more spreader should be added until the droplets run together.

The man doing the spraying must be sure that the spray covers all parts of the plant, and that the pests or diseased areas are reached. In order to get coverage of the bottom side of the leaves the spray is directed upward from the base of the plant. Pests usually are not killed unless the spray contacts them directly, and failure to control pests is often caused by poor spraying methods rather than failure of the pesticide as such. Failure to control disease can be caused by incomplete coverage of the plant with the fungicide or by spacing applications too far apart and not giving coverage to the new growth.

Hydraulic spraying may be the most economical way to apply insecticides, but considerable time is consumed in doing the spraying. It requires a great deal of labor time to make a thorough spray application, and the spray leaves an unsightly residue on the leaves and flowers. Because of the time involved in making the spray application, the spraying may be delayed until men and the necessary time are available. Such delays can lead to costly infestation of pests or disease.

For an aerosol application the pesticides are purchased in a ready-to-use container commonly called a bomb. The container must withstand high pressures because the propellant with which the pesticide is mixed is a substance that is liquid at high pressures and gaseous at lower pressures. When the valve of the aerosol container is opened the propellant turns to a gas as it leaves the confines of the container and disperses the pesticide throughout the greenhouse. The aerosol particles are so fine that complete infiltration of plants and surroundings is accomplished with one trip through the greenhouse.

Fig. 8—10. Greenhouse hydraulic sprayers are narrow enough so that they can be used in the wide walk in the house, but additional spray hose may need to be added to get to the benches serviced by narrow walks. The man doing the spraying here must be using a safe pesticide as he is not wearing any protective clothing or using a respirator. (H. D. Hudson Mfg. Co. photograph)

Fig. 8—11. In making an aerosol application of a pesticide it is directed above the plants rather than directly on the plants. The operator walks through the greenhouse for a measured length of time in order to get the right amount of material dispersed in the house. Note that the aerosol container is held during operation with the valve down, and he is well protected with gas mask, hood, coat, and gloves. (Virginia Chemicals & Smelting Co. photograph)

The rate of application is based on discharging the aerosol for a certain length of time depending on the size of the area treated. The rate of discharge from the aerosol varies with temperature, and the temperature of the aerosol and surroundings should be at least 70° for good dispersal.

Since the aerosol application is made into the air rather than directly onto the plants, enough materials must be dispersed to bring the concentration of the pesticide in the air to the right amount. The cubic contents of the greenhouse to be treated must be computed before the aerosol application is made so that the length of time to make application can be figured. If exact height measurements are not known, the average height of 10 feet can be used. Cubic contents—or volume—of the greenhouse is found by multiplying the width times the length times the height (in this instance an average height of 10 feet). For a more exact computation of the volume of the greenhouse multiply width times length times the height to the eave, and add to that one half the amount of width times length times the height from eave level to ridge. If the height of ridge above eave is not known, for a standard pitch greenhouse it should be one fourth the width of the greenhouse—for a 36-foot-wide greenhouse the height of ridge above the eave level is about 9 feet.

Aerosol applications can be made in minutes as compared to hours required for a hydraulic application. This is a convenience; in addition, it leaves no visible residue on the plants, and it can save labor as well as time. The expenditure for pesticides as aerosols often is greater, however.

Some pesticides can be vaporized from steam lines, and when this can be done it is the most economical and efficient method for applying pesticides. It leaves no visible residue on the plants. Sulfur can be vaporized from steam lines for the control of powdery mildew on roses, and materials like lindane 25, Tedion 25, Dibrom 8, and Pentac 50, can be used for the control of some pests. Rates of application are based on using a certain amount of the material per volume of space treated. The volume of the house is figured in the same way that it is for an aerosol application. The control material is painted on cold lines at the end of the day, the ventilators are closed, and then the steam is turned into the lines. Usually a series of applications a few days apart are needed.

Dusting of pesticides is one of the fastest methods of application. Very little preparation is needed, and if a good duster is used, the dust can be applied rapidly. Dusts are economical to use, but unfortunately only a limited number of pesticides are available in the form of dust. An unsightly residue is left on the leaves by dusts, too. Possibly one of the best uses of dusts is as an immediate treatment. Because of the ease in application it is possible to dust as soon as the trouble is noticed, while hydraulic spraying may have to be delayed until men and time are available, and an aerosol treatment may have to wait until the temperatures can be raised in the greenhouse or until the wind dies down.

Smoke fumigators are pesticides that are mixed with a combustible material in a can, and when the fumigator is ignited, smoke laden with the pesticides spews forth. These fumigators are put up in units for either 10,000 cubic feet or 20,000 cubic feet of space. The volume or cubic contents of the greenhouse must be figured in the same manner as for an aerosol application. The number of fumigators required for that size greenhouse are spaced evenly the length of the greenhouse, the ventilators are closed, and the fumigators are ignited. Not all pesticides can be used in fumigators, but it is a convenient method to use when it is possible. Fumigators leave no residue on leaves or flowers, but the cost of application may be more than spraying or dusting.

Oil foggers use pesticides that are mixed in oil, and this mixture is dispersed into the air as a fog by the heat generated in the fogger. Dispersion throughout the greenhouse is good; however, the fogging must be limited to times when there is no strong wind that will affect the distribution in the greenhouse. Oil fog applications can be made rapidly, and other than a slight film of oil on the plants there is no noticeable residue. Not all pesticides can be mixed with the oil and dispensed through a fogger. This limits the use of foggers, and the oil-based pesticides are expensive, too.

Fogging, misting, or dusting with high velocity air is possible. Equipment is available that uses a high velocity air stream diluting and dispersing the pesticide. These are back-pack units powered with a gasoline engine that operates a high-speed blower. The dust or the pesticide concentrate is released into the air stream, producing a fine mist or dust. The mister-dusters are efficient and economical to use, and an application can be made in a short time. The primary objection to the use of this method is that the equipment is a bit bulky to maneuver through the greenhouse walks.

• USE PESTICIDES CAREFULLY, THOROUGHLY AND WISELY

Be sure that you are aware of what effects the pesticides or fungicides may have on you and other people. Read the label carefully, and follow the label directions completely. Use protective clothing so that the material does not contact your skin, and wear a respirator or gas mask so that the vapors or dust are not breathed. Be particularly

Fig. 8—12. Years of patient research and thousands of dollars are expended for each new pesticide or fungicide that is developed. Here a scientist is evaluating a new fungicide for tomatoes. The two plants on the right were treated. The four plants to the left were not treated. (Niagara Chemical Div. photograph)

careful when mixing sprays as the material is then being handled in its concentrated form.

Know the effect of the material on the plant. The material that is used must not only control the pest or the disease, but it must be safe to use on the plant. If the label does not include recommendations for the problem at hand or the particular plant, do not use the material until you have specific recommendations from an authority.

Use the correct material for controlling the pest or disease. To do this you will first have to know which pest or disease is present and causing the problem. Disease symptoms often are quite similar. Seek the aid of the county agricultural agent or university specialists in determining the cause of the disease and the means of controlling it. More harm than good may come from guessing and using the wrong material.

Many diseases are controlled more easily by adjusting the plant surroundings than by using chemicals. Before applying disease control chemicals make sure that temperature, moisture, air movement and other environmental factors are being controlled in the best possible way for the plant.

Pests are more easily identified than diseases, but the means of control change constantly as the pests become immune or resistant to chemicals that have been used. Keep in touch with the state flower growers' association or university, or experiment station personnel for the latest recommendations for control of pests. Very often there is just one material that is currently doing a good job of controlling a certain pest, and it is better to get this information from someone who knows rather than to experiment by yourself until the right material is found.

Fig. 8—13. There are several excellent fungicides that can be used for the control of disease organisms, but the right material must be used. Quite often only one material is the best for the disease organism involved. Read the label and follow directions on methods of application. (Jednak Floral Co. photograph)

Know how and when to apply pest controls. There is some advantage in making routine, regular applications of pesticides for if the right materials are used, the plants may be kept clean of pests at all times.

The problem with this method of control is that more pesticides may be applied to the plant than are needed, and the plant may suffer from the constant use of these materials. If the plants can be watched

Fig. 8—14. Hanging the end of the hose is a simple operation, but it can save some serious disease problems. Laying the end of the hose on the ground and then placing it on the pot plants or bench soil can transfer disease organisms.

closely for the first signs of infestation and then action taken immediately, this may be the best method of control. If there is any question about being able to sight infestations early or take fast action to control them, it would be best to make general pest control applications monthly.

Be sure that the control material gets to the pest. Red spiders typically are on the under side of the leaves and more likely on the older foliage. Aphids and thrips inhabit the tips of the plant. Slugs make the trip nightly from moist locations at the ground level to feed on the succulent leaves or petals toward the tip of the stem. The pesticide needs to be applied so that it contacts the pest regardless of where it is or what its habits might be. The methods of application need to be varied to get the pesticide to the particular pest in question.

If the pest is two spotted mite, find out if the miticide controls the eggs or adults or both. If only the adults are affected, a repeat application will need to be made three to five days after the first one to control the newly hatched mites. If only the eggs are controlled, it may be necessary to make repeat applications that control the eggs until the adults die of old age.

Aphids are adept at escaping pesticides by crawling under bud scales. Repeat applications are needed to control the escapees from the first application.

Some pests continually infiltrate from outdoors. Thrips are notorious for their continual migration into the greenhouse from outdoors during thrip season. Thrip control must be just as continuous during this period. There may be migrations into the greenhouse of some strange pests from vegetable or field crops that are harvested in the fall—pests seeking a new home and new source of food. White flies often transfer their affection from tomatoes to chrysanthemum or poinsettia at that time.

GLOSSARY

ACID—Below pH 7. Most greenhouse soils are slightly acid—pH 6.0 to 6.5.

AERATED—Supplied with air.

AGGREGATE—Gravel, crushed rock, haydite or other coarse, inert material that can be mixed with soil to make the soil mixture more porous.

ALKALINE—Above pH 7. Most greenhouse soils should be slightly acid —pH 6.0 to 6.5.

ANALYSIS—Refers to fertilizer analysis that lists the per cent of nitrogen, phosphorus, and potassium in the fertilizer.

B.T.U. (British Thermal Unit)—A heat quantity that is used to express heat loss or requirement in the greenhouse.

BED—The area where the cut flower plants or the pot plants are placed for growing. Sometimes called bench.

BENCH—The area where the cut flower plants or the pot plants are placed for growing. Sometimes called bed.

BLIND WOOD—Rose stems that do not terminate with a flower.

BOILER—This may be for either hot water or steam and the heat is generated here to provide the hot water or steam for heating the greenhouse.

BRACT—Modified leaf immediately below the flower of some plants, such as the red bracts on poinsettia.

BRANCH—To produce growth of side shoots.

BREAK—A new stem starting in growth.

BREAKER—A device for attachment to a water hose that reduces the force of the water without seriously reducing the volume.

BUDDING—The vegetative reproduction of plants by placing a leaf bud of the desired plant on the root stock of another plant in such a way that the two unite and grow.

BULLHEAD—Malformed rose flower in which the center petals are short and the flower is blunt.

BUNCH—Flowers of the same kind and quality in units of 12 or 25.

BUSHY—A type of plant growth with good development of side shoots.

CALLUS—The first tissue that forms on the cut end of a cutting or at the union of scion and root stock in a graft.

CHLOROSIS—A yellowing of the leaves caused by the lack of green pigment (chlorophyll).

CIRCULATION PUMP—A pump placed in hot water lines to speed the flow of the water through the lines and provide faster heating.

CLOTH HOUSE—An outdoor growing area that is covered with cotton tobacco cloth or plastic screen to reduce the amount of sunlight.

COLD FRAME—An outdoor growing area that can be covered with glass or transparent sash.

CONDENSATE—The water that condenses as the steam cools in the heating lines. The condensate is returned to the boiler.

CONDENSATION—Water that forms on cool surfaces.

COUPLING—A pipe or hose fitting used for joining pipe or hose together.

CROP—Can refer to the kind of plant or flower or it may be used to refer to the harvest of flowers at a particular time.

CROWN BUD—A flower bud formed in conditions that are variable or at times not suitable for flower bud formation. The side buds below it are vegetative.

CUT—Commonly used as verb referring to the act of cutting flowers— also as a noun as an abbreviation for cut flowers.

CUT FLOWER—Flower that is cut from the plant and sold.

CUTTING—A vegetative portion removed (cut) from the plant for propagation.

DAMPING-OFF—A disease that affects seedlings. Several different fungus organisms may cause the disease, and the infestation is commonly at the soil line producing girdling and death of the plant.

DIBBLE—As a verb: to make a hole in the soil in which the seedling or rooted cutting is planted. As a noun: the instrument with which the hole is made.

DIRECT PLANTING—To plant rooted cuttings or seedlings directly to the bench or large flower pot.

DISBUD—As a verb: the act of removing the side (lateral) buds from a stem leaving only the terminal flower bud. As a noun: the lone flower per stem that results from removing the side buds.

DISEASE ORGANISM—Fungus, bacterium, or virus that can produce plant diseases.

DORMANT—Not in an active state of growth.

DORMANT EYE—A rose plant produced by budding; the bud (eye) is not allowed to grow in the field before the plant is shipped.

DRIP GROOVE—Groove on each side of roof bar to conduct condensation from roof to side wall.

EAVE—The point where the side wall joins the roof.

ELL—A pipe fitting that provides for change of direction. The 90° ell giving a right angle change is most common.

EVEN SPAN—Each side of the greenhouse roof is the same length.

EXPANSION LOOP—A loop placed in mains or heating lines to allow for expansion and contraction with the changes in temperature.

EYE—The vegetative bud at the node.

F-1 HYBRID—The seed that results from the transfer of pollen from a pure line parent to the pistil of a pure line parent of another type.

FEMALE THREADS—Internal threads such as on pipe fittings.

FERTILIZER—Substances that furnish chemicals that are necessary for good plant growth.

FIBERGLASS—Rigid plastic for covering plastic house.

FLAT—A tray or box approximately 15 inches by 20 inches by 2¾ inches used for carrying pot plants or filled with soil and used for sowing seed.

FLORET—The individual flower of a flower cluster. The florets may be compactly arranged as in chrysanthemum, or well spaced as in snapdragon.

FLOWER BUD—A growing portion of the plant that produces flower type growth.

FORCE—To provide the best conditions for plant growth.

FUMIGATION—Treatment of soil with chemicals that are gas in form or change to gas for control of pests, disease, and weeds. It can refer also to the use of pressure fumigators for the control of pests.

FUNGICIDE—A material used for the control or eradication of fungus organisms that cause disease.

GABLE—The end wall of the greenhouse from the eaves or gutters to the ridge.

GERMINATION—The first start of growth in a seed.

GLAZE—The act of placing and sealing the glass in the roof bars.

GRADUAL SHIFT—To plant rooted cuttings or seedlings in small pots, and then transplant to the next size larger pot until the plant is finally in the large pot in which it will be finished.

GRAFT—Vegetative propagation in which a stem portion of the plant being reproduced is joined with the roots of another plant.

GRAVITY SYSTEM—Either hot water or steam heating systems in which the boiler is at a lower level than the heating lines and the water or condensate returns by gravity.

GREENHOUSE—A structure covered with glass or other transparent material that allows enough light to enter for the good growth of (green) plants.

GROUND BENCH—A flower growing area at ground level usually with sides, but it may or may not have a bottom.

GUTTER—Placed at the eaves between attached (ridge and furrow) greenhouses to conduct away the water drainage from the roofs.

HEAD ROOM—The height of the greenhouse or the amount of space between the soil and the above structure.

HEATING LINES—Steam or hot water pipe placed in the greenhouse to distribute heat evenly.

HIGH PRESSURE MIST—A means of adding water vapor to the greenhouse air to increase the humidity and cool the air.

HOLD—To keep plants or flowers in conditions that limit their further growth or development.

HORMONE—Growth substance that influences the growth and development of plants.

HUMIDITY—The amount of moisture in the air expressed as the percent of the total amount possible.

INJECTOR—A device for injecting a uniform amount of liquid fertilizer concentrate into the irrigation water.

INORGANIC MATTER—Material that did not originate from a living thing. Fertilizer salts and aggregates such as gravel, haydite, or perlite, are examples.

INSECTICIDE—A material used for the control or eradication of insects.

INTERNODE—The portion of the stem between two nodes.

IRRIGATION—The act of supplying water to the soil.

LATH HOUSE—An outdoor growing area that is covered with lath spaced to allow penetration of about one half the light.

LEACH—To apply large quantities of water to the soil at one time to reduce the amount of fertilizer in the soil.

LEAF AXIL—The point where the leaf attaches to the stem.

LEAF BUD—The vegetative bud on the stem where the leaf attaches to the stem (leaf axil).

LIFT—The act of removing rooted cuttings from the propagation bench.

LINE—Refers to iron pipe installed the length of the greenhouse for hot water or steam heat.

LONG DAY—The dark period must be no longer than seven continuous hours.

MAINS—The pipes that conduct the hot water or steam from the boiler to the heating lines in the greenhouse.

MALE THREADS—External threads such as on pipe.

MANURE—Refuse from animals together with straw or bedding material that is used for addition to soil or as a mulch on rose soils.

MOTHER BLOCK—Plants that are used as a source of cuttings.

MYLAR—A clear, polyester plastic film used as covering for plastic houses.

NIPPLE—A short length of pipe, threaded at both ends.

NODE—The position on the stem where leaves and branches are located.

OWN ROOT—A rose rooted cutting.

ORGANIC MATTER—Either plants or animals or refuse from them.

pH—Symbol used to express the degree of acidity or alkalinity. pH 7 is neutral. Below that is acid and above alkaline.

ppm—Parts per million, a common means for expressing the amount of material in a solution or mixture. Using an insecticide at

1250 ppm is 1250 volume units of the insecticide in 1,000,000 volume units of the mixture in water, and this is using a liquid insecticide at the rate of 1 pint in a 100 gallon tank filled with water. A concentration of 300 ppm of carbon dioxide in the air is the same as 300 volume units of CO_2 per 1,000,000 air volume units or .03%.

PVC (polyvinylchloride) (vinyl)—Either film or rigid plastic for covering plastic houses.

PAD AND FAN COOLING—A method for reducing the air temperature in the greenhouse by exhausting the air with fans and allowing air to enter through moistened pads.

PEAT MOSS—Partially decayed sphagnum moss used as an addition to soil to make it more porous. Peat moss is generally acid in reaction.

PESTICIDE—A material used for the control or eradication of pests.

PESTS—Insects are the most common pests; however, greenhouse plants are bothered also by spider mites, nematodes, millipedes, and rodents.

PHOTOPERIOD—The daily light period. Photoperiodism is the effect of the light period on the development of plants.

PHOTOSYNTHESIS—The manufacture of sugar in green plants.

PIGMENT—The substance in plants that determines the color of light that is reflected.

PINCH—The act of removing the tip of the stem to promote lateral branching.

PIPE DOPE—A sealing compound placed on the pipe threads as the pipe is coupled.

PIPE FITTINGS—Various threaded attachments used for joining pipes together.

PISTIL—The female portion of the plant.

POLLEN—The dust-like particles on the male portion (stamen) of the plant that are transferred to the female portion (pistil) of the plant in sexual reproduction.

POLYETHYLENE—A film plastic used for covering plastic houses.

POT PLANT—More properly "potted plant" but common usage is pot plant. A plant that is grown and sold in a pot.

PRICK-OFF—The transplanting of seedlings from the seed flat to pots
   or other containers.

PROPAGATION—The reproduction of plants by seed, cuttings, budding
   or grafting,

PRUNE—To remove some of the stems of the plant so that fewer but
   larger flowers are produced per plant.

PURLIN—Roof members that run lengthwise to the greenhouse spaced
   equidistant between ridge and eave.

RAISED BENCH—The flower growing area elevated on legs for ease in
   working or to provide better growing conditions.

REDUCER—A pipe fitting with one outlet smaller than the other to
   provide for changing from one pipe size to another.

RETURN PUMP—A pump placed in the condensate return lines of a
   steam system to return the condensate to the boiler.

RIDGE—The top member of the greenhouse that is located at the peak.

RIDGE AND FURROW—An arrangement of greenhouses in which the
   houses are attached at the side.

ROOF BARS—Wooden or aluminum roof members spaced at the right
   width to hold glass.

ROOT STOCK—The roots or stem and roots of the plant to which a
   scion is joined in grafting or a bud in budding.

ROTATION—The succession of one crop following another so that the
   greenhouse space is fully occupied and the kinds and amounts
   of crops are produced when needed.

SCION—The stem of the plant that is joined with the root stock of
   another in grafting.

SEED FLAT—A tray or box approximately 15 inches by 20 inches by
   2¾ inches, filled with soil and used for sowing seed.

SEEDLING—A young plant that was produced from seed.

SEXUAL PROPAGATION—The reproduction of plants by seed.

SHADE—This may be incidental shade as cast by adjoining buildings or
   overhead objects. It may be intentional, partial screening of
   the sun by placing light cloth or screen above the plants, or
   by painting or spraying the exterior of the greenhouse with
   "shading compound." In some instances it refers to the use
   of black cloth over chrysanthemums to limit the length of day.

SHIFT—To transplant from a pot to a larger sized pot.

SHOOT—A young stem just starting in growth.

SHORT DAY—A day length of twelve hours or less.

SINGLE STEM—Plants that are handled in such a way that only one flowering stem is produced.

SIPHON—A simple suction device used to add liquid fertilizer concentrate to the irrigation water.

SLAT SHED—An outdoor growing area that is covered with slats spaced to allow penetration of one half the light or less.

SLEEVE—A paper or plastic film cone or cylinder to be placed around pot plants for their protection in shipping.

SOIL TEST—A test made to determine the fertilizer status of the soil.

SPORES—The means of propagation of many fungus disease organisms.

SPOT WATER—To apply water to the soil only in certain areas.

STAMEN—The male portion of the plant.

STARTED EYE—A rose plant produced by budding and the bud (eye) is started in growth in the field before the plant is shipped.

STEAM STERILIZATION—The process of steaming soil and equipment to eliminate disease organisms, pests, and weeds.

STICK—To place cuttings in the propagation bench for rooting.

STOCK PLANT—A plant that is used as a source of cuttings.

STOCKS—*Mathiola incana,* a spike-type flower grown in greenhouses and outdoors in the southwest.

SUB-IRRIGATE—To supply water to the soil from the bottom.

SYRINGE—To spray plants with water to make the surroundings more moist, to clean the leaves, or to dislodge pests.

TEE—A pipe fitting that provides for joining an additional pipe at right angles to the existing pipe.

TERMINAL BUD—A flower bud formed in uniformly suitable conditions for flower bud formation. The side buds below it are also flower buds.

THERMOSTAT—A device that can make electrical contact at a set temperature.

TRAP—Steam trap that allows condensed water but not steam to pass through.

TRUSS—The structural member that supports the roof without use of posts.

UNEVEN SPAN—One side of the green house roof is longer than the other. Used on hillsides with the short span on the top side and the long span down the hill.

UNION—A pipe fitting that is used so that the pipe can be "broken" at that point for repairs or installation of equipment.

UNIT HEATER—A combination of heating coils and fan to distribute heat evenly over an area from a central overhead location.

VASE—A container used for placing flowers in water.

VEGETATIVE BUD—As growth occurs in a vegetative bud, stem and leaves are produced.

VEGETATIVE PROPAGATION—The reproduction of plants by cuttings, budding, or grafting.

VENTILATOR—Hinged window sash located at ridge and eave that can be opened or closed for ventilation.

VINYL (polyvinylchloride) (PVC)—Either film or rigid plastic for covering plastic houses.

WATER-LOGGED SOIL—Soil saturated with water because of insufficient drainage.

INDEX